DO YOU KNO█
FILMS UPSE█
PEOPLE.' DA█
OR MAYBE EVEN MAE WEST?

CAN YOU RECALL WHICH BRITISH TOM
PLAYED A GREEK IN *SHIRLEY
VALENTINE?*

OR MAYBE YOU CAN MAKE THE
CONNECTION BETWEEN ARNOLD
SCHWARZENEGGER AND *J. F. K.*

IF THE ANSWER IS YES, YES, YES – YOU
HAVEN'T READ THE QUESTIONS
PROPERLY – BUT IF YOU THINK YOU
KNOW THEN PREPARE YOURSELF FOR
THE CHALLENGE OF THE *MOVIEWATCH
FILM QUIZ BOOK*

The Moviewatch
Film Quiz Book

—

Compiled by Will Adams

A SIGNET BOOK

SIGNET

Published by the Penguin Group
Penguin Books Ltd, 27 Wrights Lane, London W8 5TZ, England
Penguin Books USA Inc., 375 Hudson Street, New York, New York 10014, USA
Penguin Books Australia Ltd, Ringwood, Victoria, Australia
Penguin Books Canada Ltd, 10 Alcorn Avenue, Toronto, Ontario, Canada M4V 3B2
Penguin Books (NZ) Ltd, 182–190 Wairau Road, Auckland 10, New Zealand

Penguin Books Ltd, Registered Offices: Harmondsworth, Middlesex, England

First published 1994
1 3 5 7 9 10 8 6 4 2

Typeset by Datix International Limited, Bungay, Suffolk
Filmset in 9½/11½ pt Monophoto Plantin
Printed in England by Clays Ltd, St Ives plc

Movie-Watching – Getting Your Kicks from the Flicks

Very possibly the biggest publishing scoop since Sharon Stone's *Guide to Hollywood Dating*, packed with more twists, turns and surprises than Keanu's boxer shorts, and with more unanswered questions than a sequel to *JFK*, it's finally arrived: *The Moviewatch Film Quiz Book*.

Shoe-horned into 128 environmentally friendly pages, this book will provide even the most truly bodacious of movie dudes with tantalizing teasers on the directors, deals, dollars and dream-babes of Hollywood and beyond.

Excellent!

Last year over 100 million movie-watching tickets were sold in UK cinemas. And now, 267 films, much popcorn and 317 million video rentals later, this year things are looking even better for the movie-moguls. The big screen has become truly big business with more movie maniacs than ever before getting bigger kicks from better flicks.

Let loose amongst the general public for further excursions, Channel Four's *Moviewatch* has taken you around the United Kingdom at an unstoppable 24 frames a second. As our film judges, jury and occasional executioners we've trapped and tortured you for your verdicts in our weekly roving reports from Dagenham to Dundee on the week's new releases.

Every week over three million of you insisted on tuning in to discover what young Britain had to say about the hit-flicks, who was calling the shots in Hollywood, and the latest news on British releases.

The business of moving pictures is as complex as ever, with insider deals, outsiders' gossip and the global fat-cats still sitting squarely on top, looking altogether pleased with themselves. Find out more than simple small talk for less than the price of a cinema ticket with a book that gives you the full picture on the big picture.

Here, lovingly squeezed into its glossy cover, *Moviewatch*

with Signet gives you another chance to 'bluff your way as a film expert'. Which actor recommended that you 'wipe your nose and check your flies' as the first rule of acting, or who was the only Oscar to win an Oscar, or what job does a Foley artist do in film-making?

Who knows? Well probably you soon, if you own this truly immense movie fact-pack. Teasers, trivia and totally useless expertise await those needing a thorough mind-warping on the film-facts of life. Until your next visit to the moviedrome, remember, it's like Arnie says:

'We'll be back . . .'

David MacMahon, Executive Producer, *Moviewatch*

Acknowledgements
and Bibliography

When Penguin asked me if I would like to compile a movie quiz book, I needed no second bidding, so my thanks should go to them for giving me the opportunity to spend months poring over movie books, and to *Moviewatch* for providing the impetus and framework. I'm no movie authority unaided, so I must give due credit to the authors of the books I consulted. Chief amongst these is, of course, what Benny Green describes on the back cover as 'indispensable . . . it *is* one of the most fascinating books you ever saw', *Halliwell's Filmgoer's Companion* (10th edition, ed. John Walker, Harper-Collins, 1993) – with each edition it gets better and better. Alongside this, *Halliwell's Film Guide* (8th edition, ed. John Walker, Grafton, 1992) is equally invaluable.

Other books that provided me with the source material for these quizzes were, in alphabetical order: *The Chronicle of the Movies* (Hamlyn, 1991); *Empire: The monthly guide to the movies* (EMAP Metro Ltd); *The Film Encyclopaedia*, Ephraim Katz (Thomas Y. Crowell, 1979); *The Film Yearbook*, vol. 3, ed. Al Clark (Virgin Books, 1984); *Hollywood Anecdotes*, Paul F. Boller, Jr, and Ronald L. Davis (Macmillan, 1987); *The Motion Picture Annual 1990* (Cinebooks, 1990); *The Movie* (partwork) (Orbis Publishing, 1982); *Movielists*, John Koski and Mitchell Symons (Chapman's, 1992); *The Movies of the Eighties*, Ron Base and David Haslam (Macdonald, 1990); *The Pan Book of Dates*, Gerald Masters (Pan, 1990); *60 Years of the Oscars*, Robert Osborne (Equation, 1989); and finally *The Time Out Film Guide* (3rd edn, Penguin, 1993), packed with succinct and entertaining reviews of some 9,000 movies – highly recommended!

Puzzles

Look Who's Talking

Let's start with the stars. After all, as Marlon Brando said, 'An actor's a guy who, if you ain't talking about him, ain't listening.' Here are some talking about themselves – can you decide which of the three people named in each case is speaking?

1 On acting: 'Talk low, talk slow, and don't say too much.' Arnold Schwarzenegger, Sylvester Stallone or John Wayne?

2 Also on acting: 'First wipe your nose and check your flies.' Charlie Chaplin, Alec Guinness or Steve Martin?

3 'I don't want to achieve immortality through my work. I want to achieve it through not dying.' Woody Allen, Kenneth Branagh or George Burns?

4 'I know my films upset people. I *want* to upset people.' David Lynch, Ken Russell or Mae West?

5 'I made more lousy pictures than any actor in history.' Humphrey Bogart, Peter Sellers or John Wayne?

6 'I don't use any particular method. I'm from the let's pretend school of acting.' Sean Connery, Michael Douglas or Harrison Ford?

7 'If you ask me to play myself, I will not know what to do. I do not know who or what I am.' Alec Guinness, Peter Sellers or Robin Williams?

8 '. . . I'm a skilled professional actor. Whether or not I've any talent is beside the point.' Michael Caine, Mel Gibson or Eddie Murphy?

9 'When I sing, people shut up.' Liza Minnelli, Frank Sinatra or Barbra Streisand?

10 'She has that wonderful British strength that makes you wonder why they lost India.' Said of whom: Julie Andrews, Margaret Rutherford or Maggie Smith?

11 'He looks like a half-melted rubber bulldog.' Said of whom: Mel Brooks, Walter Matthau or Oliver Reed?

12 'I just put my feet in the air and move them around.' Fred Astaire, Madonna or John Travolta?

13 1956 headline: 'EGGHEAD WEDS HOURGLASS'. The 'egghead' was Arthur Miller; who was the 'hourglass': Sophia Loren, Marilyn Monroe or Raquel Welch?

14 'My acting range? Left eyebrow raised, right eyebrow raised.' Charles Bronson, Robert Mitchum or Roger Moore?

15 'I give myself to my parts as to a lover.' Glenn Close, Vanessa Redgrave or Meryl Streep?

16 'Someday I'd like a part where I can lean my elbow against a mantelpiece and have a cocktail.' Charles Bronson, Danny DeVito or Bruce Willis?

17 'People in the street still call me "Popeye". I wish I could have another hit and a new nickname.' Who's the actor, and the film referred to?

Cast of Thousands

As well as stars, movies are all about big money and big numbers. George Jean Nathan described movies as 'Ten million dollars' worth of intricate and ingenious machinery functioning elaborately to put skin on baloney.' So here's a quiz about the size and cost of that baloney . . .

1 Which highly sophisticated animation/live-action movie of 1988 listed 739 people on the credits?

2 Which 1974 disaster movie used fifty-seven sets, only eight of which survived destruction by fire or water during filming?

3 In 1989 Steven Spielberg's income was estimated at $105 million, making him the second highest paid American entertainer after – who?

4 *Raise the Titanic!* (1980) was a $36 million flop for Lord Grade. 'Raise the *Titanic*?' he said. 'It would have been cheaper to . . .' – What?

5 In 1982 Steven Spielberg bought Rosebud for $55,000. What is it, and from which movie does this bit of memorabilia come?

6 Talking of Spielberg, George Lucas's *American Graffiti* in 1973 cost $750,000 and took $55 million. How much would *Jurassic Park* need to take to be as successful? Guess!

7 In *The Ten Commandments* (1956) which event was re-created using a back-lot tank made from 30,000 cubic feet of concrete feeding a waterfall over which 360,000 gallons of water were released?

8 'The finest action sequence ever filmed' needed an

18½-acre set built from 1,000,000 feet of timber, 250 miles of metal tubing, 450 tons of plaster and 40,000 tons of sand, accommodating 8,000 extras and seventy-eight horses. What was the scene, and in which film?

9 In 1990 *Who Framed Roger Rabbit* (1988) shared the record as the most expensive movie to date ($70 million) with an all-action sequel movie of that year – which?

10 It cost only $3.8 million to make in 1939, but by 1990 had made $79.4 million. Which movie?

11 A Second World War aircraft hangar in Alabama was converted to make the largest film set to date – 450 feet long, 250 feet wide and 90 feet high – for this 1977 sci-fi blockbuster. What was the movie?

12 In 1961 a Canadian film producer bought the rights to all but one of a particular author's books, and they have so far spawned sixteen movies. Which author, and which books?

Leading Ladies

So, ladies first, I guess, and it's the leading letter of each answer that counts here. When all the answers to the clues have been placed in the grid, their initial letters will spell out the name of a leading British actress, and the numbered squares, taken in order, will spell out her recent movie hit.

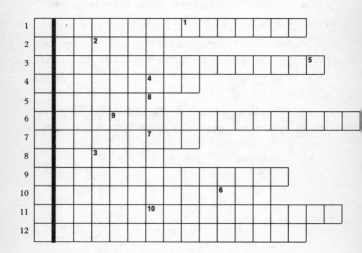

1 British-born actress, evacuated to Hollywood during the war to become a child star (9,6)

2 Controversial modern actress and singer: 'I lost my virginity as a career move' (7)

3 Once *Married to the Mob* (1988), in 1992 a Catwoman (8,8)

4 Diane Keaton title role (using her real surname) that won her an Oscar in 1977 (5,4)

5 'Dorothy Michaels' – a drag for Dustin Hoffman in this 1982 film! (7)

6 Young British actress in *A Room with a View* (1985) and *Hamlet* (1990) (6,6,6)

7 Maud Adams's title role (1983) in which she gets her tentacles on James Bond . . . (9)

8 'It's not the men in my life, it's the life in my men that counts,' purred this thirties sex symbol (3,4)

9 Willy Russell's Shirley Valentine (1989) (7,7)

10 She and Geena Davis were *Thelma and Louise* (1991) (5,8)

11 Melanie in *Gone with the Wind* in 1939, and the Queen Mum in TV movie *Charles and Diana* in 1982! (6,2,9)

12 German actress, *Tess* before joining the *Cat People* in 1982 (9,6)

Continuity

Continuity is the art of linking movie scenes so a real time-lag between shooting them is not obvious. For example, in *Anatomy of a Murder* (1959) Lee Remick leaves a café in a dress, but is wearing trousers in the next shot outside the door! I hope I've done better with this first of half a dozen quick-fire quizzes where each question is linked to the next.

1 What is 'Crocodile' Dundee's first name?

2 Who played the title role in Peckinpah's 1964 western *Major Dundee*?

3 Peckinpah's 1978 film starring 'Rubber Duck' Kris Kristofferson took its name from a contemporary popular song – which?

4 Which 'family' served us *Duck Soup* in 1933?

5 Which Duck always g-got the b-better of P-Porky P-Pig?

6 A pig was stolen by a Python in *A Private Function* (1984). Which Python?

7 Whose 'private life' was portrayed on screen by Charles Laughton in 1933?

8 Laughton played opposite Gable in 1935, and Trevor Howard opposite Brando in the 1962 remake. Which movie?

9 Brando's first Best Actor Oscar was for *On the Waterfront*. Which 1972 role earned him his second?

10 Which veteran actor and actress were *On Golden Pond* in 1981?

11 Which comedy actor was social worker to *The Golden Child* in 1986?

12 In *Child's Play* (1988) and its two sequels the spirit of a mass murderer was transferred to – what?

13 Who played the DJ asked to *Play Misty for Me* in the 1971 thriller?

14 Which real-life actress was played by lookalike Misty Rowe in a 1976 biopic?

15 Which silent-movie star was played by ballet dancer Rudolf Nureyev the following year?

16 Which Latvian ballet dancer danced and acted his way to a Best Supporting Oscar nomination in *The Turning Point* (1977)?

17 Which British stage and screen comedian's catch-phrase (and title of one of his films) was *Turned Out Nice Again* (1941)?

18 Which of the late Dick Emery's character catchphrases supplied the title of his 1972 movie?

19 Who was the 'Dick' in *Carry On Dick* (1974)?

20 Which is the odd one out: *Carry On Admiral* (1957), *Carry On Sergeant* (1958) and *Carry On Constable* (1960)?

21 Which admiral has been played on screen by Cedric Hardwicke, Laurence Olivier and Richard Johnson?

22 By what name is black actress Caryn Johnson better known?

What's in a Name?

Movie stars often have unusual or downright bizarre names, and are well known for changing them for all sorts of reasons. Here, then, is a quiz about names.

1 Both Stewart Granger and Michael Keaton changed their names for the same reason – what was it?

2 Alan Smithee has directed a dozen or so films since the 1960s, but no one has ever met him – why?

3 In *The Godfather Part II* Troy Donahue plays Merle Johnson – what's the significance?

4 What is Burt Lancaster's full first name?

5 Victor Mature, Tyrone Power, Marlon Brando, Edward G. Robinson – powerful, macho-sounding names for the screen, but all but one are the actors' *real* names. Which is the made-up one?

6 Powerful screen actor Charles Carter took his mother's maiden surname as his first name and adopted the surname of her second husband when the Carters divorced. Who is he?

7 Madonna is the singer/actress's *real* name – true or false?

8 Who did Allen Stewart Konigsberg become – Woody Allen, Alan Alda or James Stewart?

9 Scotsman Thomas took the Irish form of 'John' for his first acting job. Who is this major screen star?

10 'Bogarde' is an Anglicization of Dirk's real foreign surname – in what country was his father born?

11 Writer/producer/director Melvin Kaminsky has been

10

married to actress Anna Maria Italiano since 1964. Both hung on to their first names, more or less. Who are they?

12 British actress Joyce Frankenberg acts under the name of Henry VIII's third wife. Who is she?

13 Mr Hoar-Stevens, a well-loved British comic actor who died in 1990, was better known by his two first names, reversed and hyphenated. Who was he?

14 When American actor Val Kilmer married a British actress he added his name to hers. Who is she?

15 Meryl Streep's first name is a combination of her real first names. What are they?

16 She has been, strictly speaking, Mrs Maria Sinatra and Mrs Maria Previn. What is this actress's screen name?

17 Entrepreneurs/impresarios Barnet and Lewis Winogradsky are now respectively a peer and a knight. By what names do we know them?

It Came from Outer Space . . .

In 1980 the inept and hilarious 1956 sci-fi movie *Plan 9 from Outer Space* was awarded the title 'The Worst Film Ever Made'. Happily such movies have come a long way since then. Or have they . . .?

1 Who came from outer space according to the title of the 1985 movie scripted by and starring Mel Smith and Griff Rhys Jones?

2 Kevin McCarthy starred in this 1956 sci-fi classic, and played a cameo role in the 1978 Donald Sutherland remake. Which 'Invasion' was the subject?

3 Buster Crabbe played the role in early cinema serials, and Sam J. Jones in the 1980 big-budget feature film version. Which comic strip space hero is it?

4 Which 1968 sci-fi blockbuster begins with 'The Dawn of Man' and ends with 'Jupiter and beyond the Infinite'?

5 Which planet is *Planet of the Apes* (1967)?

6 '. . . no film with — and — in the title had ever made any money,' said the producer. It was turned down by two studios, but when it opened in 1977 the title was just those two words and it became the most profitable movie to date. Which?

7 The climax of which other 1977 sci-fi blockbuster was shot at Devil's Tower, Wyoming, the aliens being played by fifty six-year-old girls?

8 For which 1978 sci-fi movie did Marlon Brando receive $3 million for a ten-minute performance, then sue for a share of the gross?

9 In the 1981 movie *Outland* marshal Sean Connery finds himself beleaguered on Io, one of Jupiter's moons, in a sci-fi 'remake' of a famous fifties western – which?

10 *Battle beyond the Stars* (1980) also borrowed a western script, from 1960, with Robert Vaughn playing one of the assembled group in both pictures. What was the western?

11 Five years after *Star Wars* (1977) Harrison Ford found himself in 2019 LA seeking mutinous androids in a Ridley Scott movie. Title? `

12 In 1966, eleven years before his role in *Star Wars*, Peter Cushing was dealing with a race of TV spin-off aliens – which?

13 Which sci-fi title role of 1982 was actually three different creations – an actor in a padded suit, a doll attached to the floor and an electronic robot with forty different facial expressions on four interchangeable heads?

14 The 1984 movie of Frank Herbert's *Dune* was an immense flop. But who, what or where was Dune?

15 Before making *Star Trek II* (1982) Paramount undertook market research to see if audiences would tolerate a particular event concerning one of the crew members – what, and to whom?

16 It was written by H. G. Wells in 1898, Orson Welles panicked America with it on radio in 1938, and it was filmed in 1953. Which classic story is it?

The Name's the Same

Movie actors Bubba, Maggie and Mel all share the same surname – Smith. How quickly can you spot the shared name in each of these groups of three movie people?

1 Joan, Lewis and Phil.

2 Hugh, Kenneth and Melanie.

3 Jean, Judith and Lindsay.

4 George, Joe Don and Stanley.

5 Ronald, Bill and Liz.

6 John, Robin and Kenneth.

7 Sammy, Geena and Bette.

8 Ben, Don and Celia.

9 Spike, Bruce and Christopher.

10 Melvyn, Michael and Jack.

11 George, Terry and Randolph.

12 Ian, Tony and Miranda.

13 Steve, Dean and Mary.

Tom, Dick and Harry

Here's a selection of three of each gentleman, real and fictional – can you identify them all?

1 Which British Tom played a Greek in *Shirley Valentine* (1989)?

2 Which fairy tale Tom was played by Russ Tamblyn in 1958, with Peter Sellers and Terry-Thomas as the villains?

3 Which Tom provided Steve McQueen with his last but one screen role, in 1980?

4 Which director Dick (a.k.a. Richard) was responsible for *A Hard Day's Night* (1964), several *Musketeers* (1973, 1974, 1989) and a couple of *Supermans* (1980, 1983)?

5 Which Dick was a cinema serial mainstay in the thirties and forties and a starring role for Warren Beatty in 1990?

6 Which Dick was in that *Dick*, as well as *Chitty Chitty Bang Bang* (1968) and *Mary Poppins* (1964)?

7 Which bespectacled Harry provided an insubordinate early role for Michael Caine, first in *The Ipcress File* (1965)?

8 Which Harry had a theme played famously on the zither in 1949?

9 'I know what you're thinking, punk. You're thinking, did he fire six shots, or only five?' Which Harry is speaking (1971)?

Crossword No. 1

Across

1 — *for Two*, 1950 Doris Day musical (3)

3 Miss Gardner, American leading lady who died in 1990 (3)

5 Critic Barry or psycho Bates? (6)

9 Surname of the British actor/director/writer whose 1978 autobiography was *Dear Me* (7)

10 — Gossett, Oscar-winner for *An Officer and a Gentleman* in 1982 (3)

11 Hollywood production company responsible for the original *King Kong* (1933) (1,1,1)

12 Donald —, a memorable Blofeld in the Bond films (9)

13 What the cast did 'by numbers' in the 1988 Peter Greenaway movie (5)

14 *The War of the* —, 1989 Michael Douglas/Kathleen Turner movie (5)

16 She may carry a torch for you in the cinema! (9)

18 All his men provided the title for a 1976 Redford/Hoffman political thriller (9)

20 1961 Charlton Heston historical epic (2,3)

23 This actor's fiddling was over our head in the 1971 musical! (5)

24 Practice before a take? (9)

26 Kirk Douglas part cut in *Lust for Life* (1956)? (3)

27 Nightmare Street (3)

28 Actor peer whose autobiography *Confessions of an Actor* was published in 1982 (7)

29 *Enter the* —, the first Hollywood-based kung-fu movie (1973) (6)

30 — Adam, regular Bond film art director . . . (3)

31 . . . and — Hamilton, regular Bond film director (3)

Down

1 Disney rabbit, or black, athletic Bond villainess? (7)

2 3 across or down, for example (7)

3 Francesca —, Lady Macbeth on film in 1971, *Lillie* on TV (5)

4 *Bill and Ted's Excellent* — (1989) (9)

5 Nick —, American leading man in *Cape Fear* (1991), *The Prince of Tides* (1991), etc. (5)

6 Richard —, black actor best known for *Shaft* in 1971 (9)

7 First of a series of disaster movies based on an Arthur Hailey novel (7)

8 Faye Dunaway as criminal Miss Parker in 1967 (6)

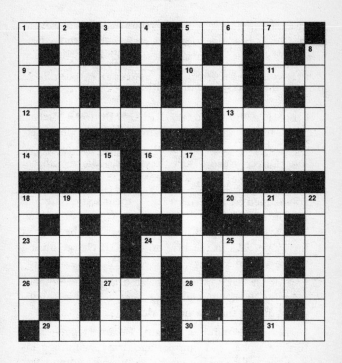

15 Director associated with sharks, cartoon rabbits and gremlins (9)

17 The 'Master of Suspense' (9)

18 Dennis —, TV playwright, also screenwriter of 1982's *Brimstone and Treacle* (6)

19 *The Last* —, 1987 Bertolucci movie with a Chinese setting (7)

21 Appointing actors to movie roles (7)

22 Roger —, rock singer who has appeared in several Ken Russell movies (7)

24 Mr Polanski (5)

25 'In space, no one can hear you scream' was this film's advertising slogan (5)

A Star is Born?

Many contemporary screen superstars had very disadvantaged – or at best unexpected – early lives! Study these brief CVs and see if you can guess which belongs to each of the following actors (two of whom are 'red herrings', just to make things more difficult!):

Mel Brooks, Yul Brynner, Richard Burton, Michael Caine, Sean Connery, Clint Eastwood, Christopher Lee, Steve McQueen, Steve Martin, Jack Nicholson, Al Pacino, Oliver Reed, Burt Reynolds, Martin Sheen, Sylvester Stallone, Gene Wilder

1 Abandoned by father as a baby, spent some time in a reform school, then drifted as sailor, lumberjack, oil field worker, carnival barker and beachcomber. Spent forty-one days in the brig on AWOL charge during war service in Marines.

2 Son of an army officer, educated at public schools, attaining fluency in eight languages. Served in Intelligence during the Second World War.

3 Father a gas pump attendant. Became logger, steel furnace stoker, gas pumper and army swimming instructor before taking course in business administration.

4 Left school and ran away from home at seventeen, becoming strip club bouncer and fairground boxer before joining Royal Army Medical Corps.

5 Raised in Peking. Balalaika player in Parisian nightclubs at the age of thirteen, then trapeze artist until bad fall.

6 Son of a Russian immigrant bottle-manufacturer. Took drama classes at college but taught fencing

18

professionally on graduating. After jobs as a chauffeur and toy salesman, he became a professional actor.

7 The twelfth of thirteen children of a Welsh coal-miner; read Classics at Oxford.

8 Father a truck-driver, mother a charlady; worked as bricklayer, lifeguard, coffin-polisher and, as body-builder, 'Mr Scotland'.

9 Father a fish market porter, mother a charlady. Left school at fifteen, worked as cement mixer and la-bourer. Got acting bug when serving tea at a London theatre.

10 At the age of ten sold Disneyland guide books – one day he sold 625, a record that earned him promotion to Merlin's Magic Shop where he performed tricks, eventually graduating to stand-up comedy.

11 A problem child from a poor broken home, he spent several years with foster parents, and was expelled from fourteen schools in eleven years. Took athletic scholarship – discouraged by drama tutors from taking any kind of acting career.

12 Of Sicilian descent, raised by his mother and grand-parents in the Bronx. Working as delivery boy, usher, porter and apartment building superintendent, he raised enough money to go to acting school.

13 Son of a police chief and former cowboy, he ran away from home at fourteen but returned and won football scholarship. Injury and a car accident caused the switch to acting. Dish-washer and bouncer while land-ing bit parts.

14 Raised by his mother, a beauty parlour owner, after his alcoholic father deserted them. Chanced on films at the age of seventeen when visiting a sister in Califor-nia; became office boy, then appeared in numerous B films.

Quiz of the Year: 1988

£ 12/76

Gene Hackman, Oscar-nominated for this year's *Mississippi Burning*, is one of the screen's hardest-working stars. 'I did nothing but work because I could never believe that an ugly schmuck like me could stay so lucky.'

1 Steven Spielberg's *Empire of the Sun* was adapted from J. G. Ballard's semi-autobiographical novel by a well-known British playwright – who?

2 Say his name three times and long-dead Michael Keaton leaps from his grave to help Geena Davis and Alec Baldwin. What was Keaton's title role?

3 In the US the Campus Crusade for Christ offered to buy the negative of this controversial Martin Scorsese picture for $10m in order to destroy it. What was the movie?

4 In which film were Eddie Valiant and the inhabitants of Toontown threatened by Christopher Lloyd?

5 'Wouldn't it be a helluva thing if this was burnt cork and you folk were being tolerant for nothing,' said the star of this year's *Coming to America*. Who is he?

6 In which movie was New York detective John McClane pitted against nasty Hans Gruber in a tower block siege?

7 The man who was Citizen Camembert ('He's the big cheese around here') in *Don't Lose Your Head* died in April. Who was the actor?

8 Another well-loved comedy actor died after falling from his horse during filming. Who was he?

9 Which comedy starred Michael Palin as 'a madly stuttering animal-loving dog-murderer' (*Time Out*)?

10 In which Mike Nichols movie were Melanie Griffith and Sigourney Weaver office rivals?

11 What, in 1988, did Sigourney Weaver as Diane Fossey have in common with David Attenborough?

12 In *Twins*, Arnold Schwarzenegger, bred in a genetic experiment as the perfect man, found he had a twin – who was less than perfect! Who played his brother?

13 Charlie and Raymond Babbitt were also newly found brothers, one of them heir to $3 million but autistic. What's the movie?

14 Linda Kozlowski appeared as Mick's girlfriend in a sequel in 1988, and married the star. Who is he, and what was his title role?

15 Tom Hanks plays a thirteen-year-old boy whose wish is granted. What, according to the movie's title, did he want to be?

16 Director Alan Parker was nominated for an Oscar for *Mississippi Burning* and Jodie Foster won one for *The Accused*. In 1976 he'd directed her when she was only thirteen – in which 'gangster' movie?

I'd Just Like to Thank . . .

Let's now take a whistle-stop tour of the last fifteen years of the Oscars, beginning in 1979, when an Awards ceremony first was a streaker running across the stage just as David Niven was about to introduce fellow pre-senter Elizabeth Taylor. 'Showing his shortcomings . . .,' as Niven said.

1979 'There are three sides to this love story' ran the Best Film's slogan; two of them, Dustin Hoffman and Meryl Streep, won Oscars. What was the movie?

1980 Three of the four acting category Oscars, won by Robert de Niro, Sissy Spacek and Mary Steenbur-gen, were unusually for a particular type of role – what type?

1981 The only book producer David Puttnam could find to read in a newly rented home was *The Official History of the Olympics*, but it was to lead to this year's Best Film. What was it?

1982 'It took one remarkable man to defeat the British Empire . . .' and by doing so 'he' won eight Oscars. Who was he?

1983 Diminutive Linda Hunt won Best Supporting Ac-tress for her role in *The Year of Living Dangerously*. But what was it about the role that made the award unique?

1984 'The Man . . . The Music . . . The Madness . . . The Murder . . .' Which composer inspired this year's Best Film?

1985 *Out of Africa* won seven of its eleven Oscar nomina-tions. *The Color Purple* also gained eleven nomina-tions. How many did it win?

1986 The Best Screenplay winner (he had also directed and starred in the movie) was, characteristically, playing clarinet in Michael's Pub in New York instead of attending the ceremony. Who is he?

1987 The Best Actor winner thanked his actor father 'for helping a son step out of a shadow'. Who are father and son?

1988 The way Dustin Hoffman's character attempted to pronounce his name Raymond provided the title for this year's Best Film. Which was it?

1989 A Special Award went to a man who started by trying to reduce background noise on LPs, but whose name has since appeared on over 2,500 films, and whose system is used in 100 studios in twenty-five countries. Who is he?

1990 This year's Best Actress was eighty years old, and she's still making movies. Who is she, and what was the picture, voted Best Film?

1991 A critical critic said, 'Costner has feathers in his hair and feathers in his head.' It still made Best Film! What was the movie?

1992 This year's Best Director was quoted: 'It's really hard to digest right now – slight pun intended.' To which film was he gruesomely referring?

1993 An actor collected his first two Oscars this year – neither for acting – after nearly forty years in the business. Who is he?

Return of the Sequel
Strikes Back Part II

When Sylvester Stallone finished *Rocky III* he announced that that was the end. 'This is definitely the final time,' he announced after *Rocky IV*. Then followed *Rocky V*. Such is the way with sequels . . .

1 'Frank Drebin is back . . .' in a 1991 sequel numbered $2\frac{1}{2}$ What is the comedy movie's title?

2 Officers Murtaugh and Riggs have appeared in three movies so far. According to the films' titles, what 'hardware' are they carrying?

3 In June 1992 he returned with two 'animals' to take nearly $48 million at the box office over a single weekend. Who is he?

4 Macauley Culkin is lost in New York in the sequel, but where, according to the title, was he in the original?

5 The first was singular, the second plural, and the third is distinguished by a small '3'. What's the movie series?

6 In 1984 the fourth film in this series was subtitled *The Final Chapter*. None the less another *four* followed. Which series?

7 *Star Trek V* was subtitled with a well-known phrase from the TV series – what was it?

8 *Return of the Jedi* was described as 'Episode 6' of the *Star Wars* saga – but what number was it actually in the series?

9 The original movie was made in 1960, but it was all of twenty-three years before '2' and '3' appeared, within three years of each other. What's the movie?

10 Another long pause – thirty-four years – separates Elizabeth Taylor in horsy film *National Velvet* (1944) and Tatum O'Neal in the sequel (1978). What was the sequel's title?

11 Nine years separate the *titles* of a sci-fi movie and its sequel, but sixteen years separate their releases. Which are they?

12 The '3' of *Jaws 3* had a special significance. What was it?

13 Which training establishment controlled by Commandant Lassard was the setting for six comedy movies in as many years during the eighties?

14 'I'll be back,' he promised in 1984, and return he did on *Judgement Day* in 1991. Who is he?

15 The second Rambo film, in 1985, was the first to carry that name, with a subtitle showing it as *Part 2* of the original 1982 movie. What was the first movie's title?

16 Who played the villain in three of the four *Superman* movies?

More Continuity

Here's another puzzle where each question is linked to the next.

1 Who played the 'Susan' that Rosanna Arquette was 'Desperately Seeking' in 1985?

2 American actress Susan acts under her married name, being ex-wife of Chris. What is their surname?

3 Which actor Christopher's 1977 autobiography was *Tall, Dark and Gruesome*?

4 Which British TV and stage comedian played a comedian opposite Jeff Goldblum as *The Tall Guy* (1989)?

5 In 1986 Goldblum appeared in a remake of a 1958 original, as a scientist transformed into a – what?

6 In the 1958 Oscars, David Lean, Alec Guinness and the movie they made together were all winners. What was the movie?

7 Which English king did Alec Guinness play opposite Richard Harris's 1970 title role?

8 Which biblical king provided an unlikely role for Richard Gere in 1985?

9 What sort of officer was Gere hoping to become in *An Officer and a Gentleman* (1982)?

10 *Gentlemen Prefer Blondes*, we were told in 1953, but who was the brunette who played opposite Marilyn Monroe?

11 In 1953 the biblical epic *The Robe* was the first movie shot in a new wide screen technique – what was its name?

12 The new long screen shape was much criticized: '. . . a formula for a funeral, or for —, but not for human beings.' What is the missing animal?

13 Which novelist wrote the original novel of the 1966 Michael Caine movie *Funeral in Berlin*?

14 In 1972 Bob Fosse won an Oscar for this musical set in 1930s Berlin – what was its title?

15 The story of which director/choreographer is supposedly told in Fosse's *All That Jazz* (1979)?

16 Who played the Al Jolson role in the 1980 remake of *The Jazz Singer*?

17 Which former comedian directed himself as comedian Alvy Singer in a 1977 movie subtitled *A Nervous Romance*?

18 Michael Douglas couldn't get anyone interested in his script for *Romancing the Stone* until which 1981 movie proved the public liked such adventure spectaculars?

19 Which Stone wrote *Conan the Barbarian* (1982) and directed *JFK* (1991)?

20 What is the connection between Arnold Schwarzenegger and J. F. Kennedy?

21 What contribution to movies has been made by Sir Malcolm Arnold?

22 Which real-life Malcolm provided the subject matter for a 1992 Spike Lee movie?

B $\frac{0}{12}$

Role Players

Each of the following trios has played the same role on screen. How quickly can you discover the common roles? We'll start with a simple one to ease you in!

1 Sean Connery, Roger Moore and David Niven.

2 Sean Connery, Errol Flynn and Kevin Costner.

3 Charlie Chaplin, Anthony Hopkins and Alec Guinness.

4 Basil Rathbone, Peter Cushing and Nicol Williamson.

5 Gary Oldman, Christopher Lee and Klaus Kinski.

6 Paul Newman, Kris Kristofferson and Emilio Estevez.

7 Elliott Gould, Robert Mitchum and Humphrey Bogart.

8 Laurence Olivier, Nicol Williamson and Mel Gibson.

9 Judy Garland, Diana Ross and Fairuza Balk.

10 Charles Laughton, Richard Burton and Sid James.

11 Jeffrey Hunter, Max von Sydow and Willem Dafoe.

12 Conversely, Jack Nicholson, Peter Cook and Ray Milland.

Title Roles

From the following clues, can you say who each of these groups is, as described by the title of the movie they appear in together?

1 Characters Dr Peter Venkman, Dr Raymond Stantz and Dr Egon Spengler, in a sci-fi comedy of 1984.

2 Hugh Laurie, Kenneth Branagh, Emma Thompson, Tony Slattery, Rita Rudner and Alphonsia Emmanuel, in 1992.

3 Mia Farrow, with Barbara Hershey and Dianne Wiest (Woody Allen, 1986).

4 John Belushi and Dan Aykroyd in a frantic John Landis chase movie of 1980.

5 Chevy Chase, Steve Martin and Martin Short as a trio of buddies in Mexico in a 1986 take-off of *The Magnificent Seven*.

6 Kevin Costner, Sean Connery, Andy Garcia and Charles Martin Smith in a 1987 Brian De Palma police story.

7 Conmen Michael Caine and Steve Martin in a 1988 Frank Oz comedy.

8 Bachelors Tom Selleck, Steve Guttenberg, Ted Danson and 'Mary' in 1987.

9 Ageing ex-cons Burt Lancaster and Kirk Douglas in a 1986 nostalgic caper comedy.

10 Cher, Susan Sarandon and Michelle Pfeiffer under the influence of Jack Nicholson in 1987.

Film Clips

Here's the first of a trio of quick-fire trivia quizzes to test your general movie knowledge.

1 In the industry they're known as 'group jeopardy' movies. By what more popular name do we know the genre?

2 Which 1974 train had Ingrid Bergman, Lauren Bacall, Wendy Hiller, Sean Connery, Vanessa Redgrave and John Gielgud as passengers?

3 'This is Benjamin – he's a little worried about his future.' Dustin Hoffman was Benjamin – in which 1967 movie?

4 Which 1993 Kenneth Branagh movie is subtitled 'A romantic comedy for anyone who's ever been in love'?

5 Where did insomnia strike Tom Hanks and Meg Ryan in another 1993 movie?

6 At which film festival is the Palme d'Or the premier award?

7 Which 1993 Michael Douglas film has 'Kid with Missile Launcher' amongst the cast credits?

8 Which musician/actor's first film was a Children's Film Foundation production, *Calamity the Cow*, when he was sixteen?

9 In *Back to the Future 2* (1989) a cinema of the future is showing *Jaws 19*, directed by Max Spielberg. Who's he?

10 Originally written for Steve McQueen in the 1960s,

the role eventually went to Kevin Costner. In which 1991 movie?

11 *The Hand That Rocks the Cradle* was a 1991 thriller — but can you complete the other half of the quotation from which the movie takes its title?

12 Oliver Hardy was descended from the famous Captain Hardy who kissed the dying Nelson aboard the *Victory* — true or false?

13 In the USA, 2 February is a festival providing the title for a 1993 Bill Murray comedy — which?

14 Which movie star released a soul album called *The Return of Bruno* in 1987?

15 How many seasons of Barry Norman's *Film* . . . programme have there been to date?

16 What kind of firm is *The Firm* in the 1993 Tom Cruise movie?

17 Which British comic's big-screen debut was *Trouble in Store* in 1953?

18 What is the name of the tourist attraction set up by billionaire John Hammond 120 miles off Costa Rica in the 1993 movie of the same name?

19 Who did Bob Hoskins and John Leguizamo translate from the small to the big screen in 1993?

20 In 1991 Warren Beatty played gangster Benny Siegel. What is his nickname that gives the movie its title?

Crossword No. 2

Across

8 and 9 across   Actress who starred in *Body Heat* (1981) and *Peggy Sue Got Married* (1986) (8,6)

10 Mr Beatty, Miss MacLaine's brother (6)

11 They brought up a baby in 1987 (5,3)

13 He awards film certificates (6)

15 — *Party*, 1984 Tom Hanks movie (8)

16 How Tarzan copied his jungle 'parents'? (4)

17 Trap fallen into by Hayley Mills in 1961 (6)

19 Gerald —, cartoonist who designed the animation for *Pink Floyd: The Wall* (1982) (6)

22 *The — Angel*, Marlene Dietrich's 1930 catapult to stardom (4)

23 Word used to describe movies of more than about thirty-five minutes long, as opposed to 'shorts' (8)

25 The late Miss Hepburn (6)

27 *The — —*, 1983 college reunion film starring Tom Berenger and Glenn Close (3,5)

30 Hello, Dolly, in *Nine to Five* (1980) (6)

31 Truman —, US novelist who appeared in *Murder by Death* in 1976 (6)

32 Scripted conversation between actors (8)

Down

1 Harm was done by Jeremy Irons and Juliette Binoche in 1992 (6)

2 Cyd —, the former Tula Ellice Finklea . . . (8)

3 Was Sir David inclined to direct major films? (4)

4 The second one usually provides the film with its scenic or action sequences (4)

5 Julie Andrews in a biopic of Gertrude Lawrence in 1968 (4)

6 Novelist whose filmed works include *Brighton Rock* (1947), *The Third Man* (1949) and *Our Man in Havana* (1959) (6)

7 See 18 down

12 Psychedelic 1968 'trip' movie starring the Monkees (4)

13 Arnie was one in a kindergarten in 1990 (3)

14 Animal – one of many appearing in *Willard* (1971)! (3)

15 Jennifer — , star of *Flashdance* (1983) (5)

18 and 7 down   *An — — in London*, 1981 John Landis spoof horror film (8,8)

19 It was cruel to Jack Hawkins in 1953 (3)

20 *The — Tapes*, 1971 Sean Connery thriller (8)

21 Ron —, athlete who was TV's Tarzan and *Doc Savage* on screen in 1975 (3)

22 Tom —, gaunt British film actor who was *Out* on TV (4)

24 *The Last —*, 1976 Hollywood film about Hollywood (6)

26 1960 biblical–sounding epic based on a Leon Uris novel (6)

28 Burl —, actor and ballad-singer in *Cat on a Hot Tin Roof* (1958), *The Big Country* (1958), etc. (4)

29 Alan, 1940s tough guy, or more recently Cheryl or Diane (4)

30 *— Misty for Me*, 1971 Clint Eastwood thriller (4)

The Numbers Game

Each of the following clues leads to the title of a film that includes a number between 1 and 50. The only clue you have is that each number is higher than the one in the preceding question.

1 Jack Nicholson as a con-man in a 1975 state mental hospital.

2 In 1967 Morecambe and Wise added up to fewer than Yul Brynner, Steve McQueen and Co. in 1960!

3 Number of days of Robert Redford's CIA codename in 1975.

4 1981 film starring, written by and directed by Alan Alda – shades of Vivaldi?

5 Jack Nicholson again, as a drifter who jilts his mistress for his brother's fiancée in 1970.

6 1954 Howard Keel/Jane Powell western musical, doubly numerical!

7 Beginning of a day's work in 1980 for misses Fonda, Parton and Tomlin.

8 Richard Attenborough as murderer Christie in 1971.

9 Date that provided eight horror movies between 1980 and 1989.

10 Robert Donat mounted them in 1935, Kenneth More in 1959 and Robert Powell in 1978.

11 1933 chorus-girl-to-Broadway-star Busby Berkeley musical.

12 Time available to Nick Nolte and Eddie Murphy in 1982.

The Alphabet Game

In this puzzle each clue leads to a film title that begins with an initial, and is sometimes made up of only initials – but it is the first we are interested in. The only clue we give you is that they are all in alphabetical order – but the first is not A!

1 1988 thriller with Dennis Quaid and Meg Ryan in which a poisoned professor has 48 hours to solve his own murder.

2 'The most moving science-fiction movie ever made on earth' – The *New Yorker*'s review of this 1982 Spielberg classic.

3 Orson Welles lectures the audience on truth and falsehood in a 'monologue' of 1973.

4 Elvis Presley as a guitar-playing gunner with the American Army in West Germany in 1960.

5 Kevin Costner investigating a political assassination in 1991.

6 Narcotics cop James Belushi teaming up with an alsation in 1988.

7 1962 low-life melodrama written and directed by Bryan Forbes, and set in a lodging house.

8 Comedy in which Julie Andrews bares more than usual, directed by her husband Blake Edwards in 1981.

9 Kathleen Turner as the tough feminist private eye of the title in a 1991 thriller.

10 Radio station providing the title of a 1970 Paul Newman/Joanne Woodward movie.

The Fresh Connection

In the first of two 'common links' quizzes, can you discover what each of the following groups has in common?

1 *The Elephant Man*, *Stardust Memories* and *Raging Bull* (apart from all being made in 1980).

2 Hayley Mills in *The Parent Trap* (1961), Jeremy Irons in *Dead Ringers* (1988) and Sean Young in *A Kiss Before Dying* (1991).

3 *West Side Story* (1961), *Kiss Me Kate* (1953) and *Prospero's Books* (1991).

4 Peter Sellers in *Soft Beds, Hard Battles* (1973), Alec Guinness in *Kind Hearts and Coronets* (1949) and Rod Steiger in *No Way to Treat a Lady* (1968).

5 *The Odd Couple* (1968), *M★A★S★H* (1970) and *Paper Moon* (1973).

6 'A Groovy Kind of Love', 'Take My Breath Away' and '(Everything I Do) I Do It For You'.

7 Marlon Brando, Doris Day and Eddie Murphy (especially the first two!).

8 Shirley Bassey, Sheena Easton and Carly Simon.

9 Stan Laurel, Bob Hope and Cary Grant.

10 Hooch, Toto and Asta.

11 Lionel Newman, Jerry Goldsmith and Michael Kamen.

12 Cuthbert J. Twillie, Elmer Prettywillie and W. C. Fields.

13 The Khasi of Kalabar, Citizen Camembert and W. C. Boggs.

14 Honeychile Rider, Holly Goodhead and Domino.

15 Don Johnson and Melanie Griffith, Robert Wagner and Natalie Wood, and Elizabeth Taylor and Richard Burton.

16 *Blackmail*, *Murder* and *Frenzy*.

17 *Chariots of Fire*, *Evil under the Sun* and *Empire of the Sun*.

18 The Jedi, the Pink Panther and the Living Dead.

19 Winston, Sherlock Holmes and Frankenstein.

20 Zanzibar, Morocco and Bali.

Quiz of the Year: 1989

Al Pacino made his name in the early seventies, but re-emerged in the late eighties in a number of successful movies, including *Sea of Love* (1989). 'I'm coming back, out of hibernation. It's going to be interesting to see how the audience accepts me back.'

1 Amy Irving divorced her movie director husband with a record settlement figure of around $100m. Who is her ex-husband?

2 The cost of filming the tall tales of a German nobleman soared to about twice its original budget for director Terry Gilliam. What was the movie?

3 A fictional American city was built on most of the eighteen sound stages at Pinewood – for which blockbusting movie?

4 To which Society did schoolmaster Robin Williams introduce his pupils at an élite Vermont prep school?

5 What, on his 'Last Crusade', did Indiana Jones have in common with Monty Python?

6 Columbia Pictures was bought for $3.4 billion by a Japanese company – which?

7 *Honey, I Shrunk the Kids* – but how many kids were shrunk by Rick Moranis?

8 Michael Douglas was a corrupt New York cop in Osaka, Japan, in a movie whose title referred to post-Hiroshima fall-out. What's the movie?

9 Ghostbuster Stantz went straight as Miss Daisy's son in *Driving Miss Daisy*. Who's the actor?

10 In preparation for *Henry V*, Kenneth Branagh needed to know what it would be like to be a young man suddenly made king. Who, appropriately, did he ask?

11 Which movie of marital breakdown was directed by Danny DeVito, who also appeared as the couple's divorce lawyer?

12 In which movie did Michael J. Fox play three roles: a father, his son and his daughter?

13 In which film did Keanu Reeves and Alex Winter encounter Napoleon, Billy the Kid, Socrates, Freud, Genghis Khan, Joan of Arc and Beethoven?

14 *Family Business* featured three generations of New York crooks: Matthew Broderick, Dustin Hoffman as his father, and who as Hoffman's father?

15 *The Little Mermaid* was Disney's first animated fairy tale since 1959, when the subject had been – what?

16 Mel Blanc died in July, having been heard but not seen in some 3,000 films – how come?

The Singer and the Role

'I don't really think the film business is all it's cracked up to be ... It's still much better being a guitar player.' So says former Beatle George Harrison, now a film producer with HandMade Films. Many well-known popular musicians have appeared in movies in non-singing roles, some more successfully than others. Here are a few.

1 One half of a famous duo made a brief appearance in *Annie Hall* (1977) as recording tycoon Tony Lacey; the other made his acting debut in *Catch 22* (1970). Who are they?

2 Which blonde American singer appeared in the David Cronenberg horror movie *Videodrome* in 1983, amongst others?

3 Which former singer starred with Barbra Streisand in the 1976 remake of *A Star is Born*?

4 The same singer starred in the 1973 Peckinpah western *Pat Garrett and Billy the Kid* with cult musician Robert Zimmerman. By what name is the latter internationally known?

5 Which rock singer played a real-life villain in a 1980 film co-scripted by its namesake and co-produced by the singer's band?

6 Which rock singer was involved in the Great Train Robbery on screen, and in which 1988 movie?

7 Roger Waters of Pink Floyd scripted and scored their 1982 film *The Wall*, but it starred the leading singer from another band – who?

8 Which rock singer first *Fell to Earth* in 1976, and was in the *Twin Peaks* movie in 1992?

9 Which British pop idol appeared in *Two a Penny* in 1968, a 'message' movie sponsored by the Billy Graham movement?

10 Which country singer shared *True Grit* with John Wayne in 1969?

11 'George Burns is God ... and — doesn't believe it either.' Which country singer's name is missing from the poster blurb for his 1977 debut?

12 Which American rock singer turns up as 'Auntie' in *Mad Max beyond Thunderdome* (1988)?

13 Which rock singer, bearded and helmeted, made his movie debut in 1970 as an 1870s outlaw?

14 Which 1973 film about fifties rock 'n' roll featured David Essex, Ringo Starr, Billy Fury and Keith Moon?

15 *Charro!* (1969) was rare amongst this singer's thirty-three movies – he only sang over the titles. Who was he?

16 Which former 'Policeman' made his movie debut as 'Ace Face' in the Who's *Quadrophenia* in 1979?

Know the Score

Music is, of course, very important in a movie, and composers are highly regarded. Walt Disney was delighted in particular by his choice of Beethoven's *Pastoral Symphony* for *Fantasia*. 'Gee!' he exclaimed. 'This'll make Beethoven!'

1 Which 1964 Roy Orbison hit song provided the title for a 1990 hit film?

2 In 1977 *Saturday Night Fever* featured music by the Bee Gees, and the 1983 sequel took the title of another featured Bee Gees song – which?

3 What nationality is movie composer Vangelis?

4 *Pink Floyd: The Wall* (1982) – was it the album of the film, or the film of the album?

5 For the musical score of which 1982 biopic was sitar virtuoso Ravi Shankar nominated for an Oscar?

6 Which French composer won Oscars for his music for *Doctor Zhivago* (1965) and *A Passage to India* (1984)?

7 Another French composer won an Oscar for his score for the 1983 Barbra Streisand musical *Yentl*. Who is he?

8 Mark Knopfler wrote the scores for *Local Hero* (1983) and *Last Exit to Brooklyn* (1989), amongst others – of which British rock band is he a founder member?

9 Stewart Copeland wrote the score for *Wall Street* (1987), etc. What does he have in common with actor Sting?

10 Which husband and wife team wrote the title song for the 1973 Bond movie *Live and Let Die*?

11 John Barry has written the score for twelve of the eighteen movies in a well-known series – which series?

12 Henry Mancini gained an Oscar nomination for his score for the first movie in 1963, then went on to provide the music for five of the six sequels – which series?

13 From *Valley of the Dolls* in 1967 to *JFK* in 1991, this composer has gained seventeen Oscar nominations, winning three, *Jaws* amongst them. Who is he?

14 Italian composer Ennio Morricone became well known for his scores featuring vocal, whistling and whip-crack additions – for which type of movie originally?

15 Which 1968 sci-fi blockbuster opened with music by Richard Strauss and ended with music by Johann Strauss?

16 Which British classical composer wrote the scores for the Olivier films *Henry V* (1944), *Hamlet* (1948) and *Richard III* (1956)?

Yet More Continuity

Another linked chain of movie posers.

1 Steve Martin starred in the screen version of *Pennies from Heaven* in 1981 – which actor had taken the role in the original TV serial?

2 In *All of Me* (1984), Steve Martin provides the body, but which actress provides his voice for much of the movie?

3 Which actual event formed the basis for the movie *All the President's Men* (1976)?

4 Which president starred in the wartime drama *King's Row* (1941)?

5 Which heavyweight American actor became *King Ralph* of England when the Royal Family was accidentally electrocuted in the 1991 movie?

6 One of Sir Ralph Richardson's last film roles, in 1984, was with Paul McCartney and Ringo Starr, of all people. What was the movie?

7 One of the former Beatles wrote the score for the 1986 Madonna movie *Shanghai Surprise* – who?

8 Madonna's then husband starred opposite her in the movie. Who is he?

9 The Raymond Chandler classic *The Big Sleep* (1946) starred Humphrey Bogart and his wife. Who was she?

10 The 1978 Michael Winner remake had Sarah Miles in the female lead; who played Philip Marlowe?

11 Michael Winner directed his young actress wife in *A Chorus of Disapproval* in 1989. Who is she?

44

12 Who starred in *A Chorus Line* (1985) before *Falling Down* (1993)?

13 With whom was Robert de Niro *Falling in Love* in 1984?

14 Robert de Niro appeared in a 1991 remake, but Gregory Peck, Robert Mitchum and Martin Balsam appeared in both the 1962 original *and* the remake. What's the movie?

15 Gregory Peck starred in the 1961 British actioner *The Guns of Navarone*. Who, what or where was Navarone?

16 The theme song from *Top Gun* (1986) is now better known from a car manufacturer's TV adverts. What is it?

17 Which short-lived US TV series spawned the 1988 spoof police movie *The Naked Gun*?

18 *Barefoot in the Park* (1967) starred Redford and Fonda in a screen version of a stage play by whom?

19 In the same year Jane Fonda went rather more than barefoot into a 40th-century space fantasy. What was its title?

20 Fonda was then married to the movie's director, Roger Vadim. Which French actress had he earlier discovered and married in the 1950s?

21 Vadim remade the movie that made his first wife an international star thirty years later in 1987, with Rebecca De Mornay. What title was carried by both films?

22 In 1991 Miss De Mornay was in *Backdraft*. With which public service was it concerned?

Crossword No. 3

Across

4 *Ground— Day*, 1992 Bill Murray movie (3)

8 1986 desert island movie starring Oliver Reed and Amanda Donohoe (8)

9 *—head*, 1976 David Lynch horror film (6)

10 French fashion designer whose life was filmed in 1981withMarie-FrancePisier and Timothy Dalton (6)

11 Robert Redford was such a horseman in 1979 (8)

13 *The — Game*, acclaimed 1992 Neil Jordan film (6)

15 City in which Burt Lancaster and Susan Sarandon became involved in 1981 (8)

16 Kirk Douglas was an ace in one in this celebrated 1951 movie (4)

17 Garbo's was almost her downfall when talkies arrived! (6)

19 Wes —, director of *A Nightmare on Elm Street* (1984), etc. (6)

21 Mr Mostel (4)

22 Rex – or Ford? (8)

24 Buster —, the original Flash Gordon (6)

26 *The —*, third of the Dirty Harry movies (1976) (8)

29 *A — of Seasons*, 1980 Shirley MacLaine/Anthony Hopkins movie (6)

31 *— Royale*, with David Niven as Sir James Bond in 1967 (6)

32 Leading movie actor or actress (4,4)

33 Ground upon which film sets, etc., are built (3)

Down

1 Relationship of Steve Martin to the bride in a 1991 remake (6)

2 Mr Laurel (4)

3 and 21 *— —: The Movie* – TV series brought to the screen by Landis, Spielberg, etc., in a 1983 compilation movie (8,4)

4 Over-the-top movie publicity? (4)

5 Richard —, star of *Sommersby* in 1992 (4)

6 This character had lust for glory, but George C. Scott didn't have lust for the Oscar! (6)

7 Sean Connery was such a man in 1992 (8)

12 *The — Show* was enjoyed by Art Carney and Lily Tomlin in 1977 (4)

14 *— Station Zebra*, 1968 Alistair MacLean thriller (3)

15 1979 Ridley Scott sci-fi movie (5)

18 Implement used for a 1974 massacre! (8)

19 Drinks company that used to own Columbia Pictures (4-4)

20 Miss Gardner (3)

21 See 3 down

23 1990 movie in which ageing cop Clint Eastwood teaches young new partner Charlie Sheen (6)

25 1987 film café that transferred to TV with Whoopi Goldberg (6)

27 — *Hand Luke*, 1967 Paul Newman title role (4)

28 George —, coin-flicking gangster of the thirties and forties (4)

30 *The Sun — Rises*, 1957 movie based on an Ernest Hemingway novel (4)

Opposites

Each of these clues leads to a pair of movie titles that contain 'opposites'; for example, *On the Water*FRONT and BACK *to the Future*.

1 A 1978 rabbity animation and Frankie Howerd in a 1970 Roman TV spin-off.

2 Bob Hoskins's Friday (1980) and two movies (1986 and 1988) featuring a comic military robot called No. 5.

3 Bogart's 1946 sleep and Jodie Foster's 1991 man Tate.

4 Art Garfunkel's chronological co-ordination in 1980 and Robin Williams's greeting to Vietnam in 1987.

5 The 'Brat Pack' in a 1988 re-telling of the Billy the Kid story and a long series of thirties and forties films about an Irish washerwoman.

6 1991 send-up of *Top Gun* and Richard Burton as a returning spy in 1965.

7 1979 Disney deep space adventure and real-life Kenya murder scandal with Charles Dance and Greta Scacchi in 1987.

8 1989 Spielberg movie with Richard Dreyfuss returning as the ghost of a Second World War pilot and Sean Connery returning as 007 in 1983.

9 1973 Edward Fox movie about a de Gaulle assassination attempt and the Marx Brothers at the opera in 1935.

10 1959 Cary Grant/Hitchcock thriller and the previous year's screen version of a Rodgers and Hammerstein musical.

It's Alive!

Occasionally non-human creatures – even mechanical objects – assume title roles in movies. From the following clues can you identify the name and type of animal or object, each named in a movie title?

1 With a mind of his own, he rode again, went to Monte Carlo, and went bananas in the late 1970s.

2 He was the biggest in the world, according to the title of this 1973 British comedy with Jim Dale and Spike Milligan.

3 He was brought back from Africa by a little girl, but caused panic in the city in 1949.

4 He was a high-flyer who wanted to move faster – a very successful book transferred to the screen in 1973.

5 She travelled to Brighton in 1953 to the strains of a famous harmonica accompaniment.

6 She was beloved of Michael Palin in a 1988 Charles Crichton comedy.

7 Talkative hero of seven American comedies of the 1950s.

8 He was the drinking partner of James Stewart in 1950, though no one could see him.

9 He was adopted by the Hendersons in this 1987 film after they bumped into him on holiday.

10 Far from home, he phoned home from LA in 1982.

11 A 'classical musician' who joined Charles Grodin's family in 1992 and wrought havoc, although emerging a hero.

Something Wicked This Way Comes . . .

The 1931 version of *Frankenstein* was so chilling that theatre audiences went home in a state of fright and shock. One member of the audience repeatedly phoned the cinema manager every five minutes during the night, saying, 'I can't sleep because of that picture, and you aren't going to either.' Over sixty years later, the horror goes on . . .

1 The principal character of which movie series, begun in 1984, is sometimes irreverently referred to as 'Old Pizza Face'?

2 One of the most famous horror movie actors was a gentle cricket-loving, public-school-educated Englishman born in Dulwich in 1887 as William Henry Pratt. By what name is he better known?

3 In 1980 director John Carpenter had the ghosts of shipwrecked sailors terrorizing a town, helped by what kind of weather?

4 The *Horror* came first, in 1979, *The Possession* was second, in 1982, and the third, in 1983, was in 3-D. Which series?

5 What familiar horror ingredient was awakened by Charlton Heston in *The Awakening* in 1980?

6 1980 abounded with '. . . ings': in *The Shining* we saw Jack Nicholson and his axe, while *The Howling* dealt with another group of horror film creatures – which?

7 According to the titles of the Hammer films,

Frankenstein (1957), the *Mummy's Tomb* (1964) and the *Werewolf* (1960) all had one – what?

8 Heather O'Rourke played little Carol Anne in a series of horror movies between 1982 and 1988, but tragically died during emergency surgery at the age of thirteen just after the third came out. Which were the films?

9 In which 1984 horror movie do we encounter mogwais, cute furry creatures – until splashed with water . . .?

10 'Well – a boy's best friend is his mother,' says the central character of a famous 1960 horror movie, ironically. What's the movie, and who's the son?

11 Which 1976 horror movie concerns the adopted son of the US ambassador to Britain (Gregory Peck)?

12 A mad scientist develops man-eaters for use in Vietnam, but they escape . . . Which fish give their name to this 1978 Joe Dante movie?

13 *976-Evil* was the 1988 directorial debut of actor Robert Englund. In the guise of which horror character is he more familiar?

14 Which part of Michael Caine's anatomy was severed and went on the rampage according to the title of the 1981 Oliver Stone movie?

15 What does the killer 'Jason' wear on his head in the *Friday the 13th* movies?

16 What protrude from the head of the horrific character in Clive Barker's *Hellraiser* movies?

A to Z of Movies

Each of the following clues leads to a one-word movie title beginning with successive letters of the alphabet from A to Z. However, five letters are not featured. Discover which they are – then, taken in alphabetical order, they will spell out the single-word title of a 1990 movie.

1 1984 film version of Peter Shaffer's play about Mozart.

2 1968 Steve McQueen classic with a famous car chase through San Francisco.

3 Jack Nicholson and Faye Dunaway in the Oriental quarter in 1974.

4 Disney circus cartoon feature of 1941.

5 Soft-focus 1974 Sylvia Kristel movie that spawned several sequels and spoofs.

6 1940 Disney classic restored and re-issued in 1990.

7 Anarchic 1968 Lindsay Anderson school movie starring Malcolm McDowell.

8 1975 Spielberg movie from a Peter Benchley novel.

9 1971 thriller starring Donald Sutherland and Oscar-winning Jane Fonda as a call-girl.

10 Controversial 1962 movie of a Nabokov novel starring James Mason and Shelley Winters.

11 Ventriloquist Anthony Hopkins possessed by his dummy in 1978.

12 1976 'TV movie' that won a posthumous Oscar for Peter Finch.

13 1982 horror film written and produced by Spielberg about a spirit emanating from a TV set.

14 The Who's 1979 musical about Mods and Rockers in sixties Brighton.

15 'Part man. Part machine. All cop.' Peter Weller in armour in 1987.

16 Clint Eastwood's 1992 Oscar-winning western.

17 1981 POW football movie with Sylvester Stallone, Pele, Bobby Moore, etc.

18 Smith & Jones's 1989 screen adaptation of a Tom Sharpe novel.

19 1980 musical starring Olivia Newton-John and Gene Kelly.

20 Barbra Streisand as a Jewish-Polish girl getting on by dressing as a boy in 1983.

21 Woody Allen parody documentary of 1983, with nonentity Allen apparently hobnobbing with Hitler, Roosevelt, etc.

More Film Clips

A further selection of trivia 'out-takes' to stretch your movie knowledge.

1 In 1932 the average movie was $1\frac{1}{2}$ hours long. How long was the average in 1990?

2 Which British royal is played by Quentin Crisp in the movie adaptation of Virginia Woolf's *Orlando* (1993)?

3 Which movies formed parts 4, 5 and 6 of a proposed nine-part series, between 1977 and 1983, the rest still waiting to be made?

4 A cousin of Ian Fleming played the villain in the 1974 Bond movie *The Man with the Golden Gun*. Who is he?

5 Robert Redford owns and runs a movie 'Institute' in the wilds of Utah, named after perhaps his most famous film role – which?

6 Which 1992 cult thriller features Mr White, Mr Pink, Mr Blonde and Mr Orange?

7 In *The Muppet Christmas Carol* (1992) Michael Caine is Scrooge, but who plays Bob Cratchit?

8 Which 1971 Kubrick movie hasn't been available for screening in the UK for twenty years, at its director's insistence?

9 Gaumont cinemas were named after a Frenchman, Léon Gaumont – true or false?

10 What was the family name of Dustin Hoffman, Meryl Streep and Justin Henry in the 1979 courtroom drama?

11 He was first noticed when, while still at college, he made a 24-minute short called *Amblin'*, which has become the name of his production company. Who is he?

12 What was unusual about the screenplay for the sixteenth Bond film, *Licence to Kill* (1989)?

13 Who was to have taken the Indiana Jones role, but was prevented by TV commitments, although he went on to make the less successful *High Road to China* (1983)?

14 A poor kid from the Hell's Kitchen area of New York sat down and wrote the script of the original *Rocky* (1976) in just three days. Who was he?

15 Which Austrian-born actor's surname, translated literally, means 'black ploughman'?

16 Which Dutch-born actor in action movies is sometimes called the 'Paul Newman of Holland'?

17 *Blazing Saddles* (1974), *High Anxiety* (1977) and *Spaceballs: The Movie* (1987) are all send-up spoofs of classic movies, written and directed by whom?

18 In 1977 Anthony Daniels and Kenny Baker were likened to Laurel and Hardy, although we never saw them 'in the flesh'. Which roles in which movie?

19 Which influential 1973 George Lucas movie was shot during twenty-eight nights, cost less than $750,000 but grossed $55 million?

20 *Zulu* (1963) and *Zulu Dawn* (1979) were early movie appearances for two cockney actors – name either (or both!).

Quiz of the Year: 1990

1990 was the year of Julia Roberts, who found international stardom almost by accident. 'I never really made it to acting school. I went to acting classes a few times, but it never seemed very conducive to what I wanted to do.'

1 'Mean. Green. And on the screen.' Who were they?

2 In which movie did Hollywood hooker Vivian Ward and business tycoon Edward Lewis begin an unlikely romance?

3 *Repossessed*, starring Leslie Nielsen, was a spoof of a famous 1973 movie, and starred the actress who made her name in the original. What was it?

4 A screen legend died in April, almost fifty years after her last screen appearance. Who was she?

5 In which movie did Patrick Swayze die, then come back to protect Demi Moore?

6 Meanwhile, Miss Moore was worried about her husband acting with a rather too attractive Belgian actress in *Hudson Hawk*, so had her replaced by Andie Mac-Dowell. Who's the husband?

7 Chantoose 'Breathless Mahoney' sang four new Sondheim numbers in *Dick Tracy*. Who's the actress?

8 'They stole his mind. Now he wants it back.' In which futuristic movie did Schwarzenegger remember a trip to Mars?

9 A controversy over the awarding of 'X' ratings to movies in America led to the new 'NC–17' category. What does it mean?

10 Nicholas Cage was *Wild at Heart* in 1990. Cage changed his surname to disassociate himself from his uncle Francis. What's his real surname?

11 In *Flatliners*, Keifer Sutherland and Julia Roberts conducted bizarre medical experiments in order to briefly 'flatline'. What is 'flatlining'?

12 Two criminal brothers were brought to the screen with the co-operation of their real-life originals. Who were they?

13 Martin Scorsese made *GoodFellas*, taking the title from a term used by members of an organization to describe each other. Which organization?

14 *Variety* punningly dismissed it as 'A misfire of inanities'. What was the actual title of this movie flop?

15 Kevin Costner's directorial début saw him as a soldier joining the Sioux. What did they call him, giving the movie its title?

16 Macauley Culkin was left *Home Alone* when his parents went away for Christmas. Where had they gone?

Strange Interlude

———

'What's history going to say about the movies?' mused Robert Mitchum. 'All those rows of seats facing a blank screen? Crazy!' So here's a fairly quirky quiz about some of the stranger aspects of the movie business.

1 Assuming the characters were the same age as the actors playing them, how old was Dr Henry Jones when his son 'Indie' was born?

2 In *To Have and Have Not* (1945) Lauren Bacall's singing voice was dubbed. What was unusual about the well-known singer used?

3 Which TV cop and film heavy has an MA in Psychology from Columbia University?

4 In 1992 a French actor playing a famous Italian explorer and sailor was directed in Spain by a British director. Who was the historical figure being celebrated in this multinational mix?

5 Similarly, in 1979 a Pole directed a German actress as the English heroine of a famous Victorian novel, with Northern France standing in for Dorset. What was the film?

6 In 1992 Geraldine played her grandmother Hannah in a film about her father Charles. What's the family name?

7 '— talks!' announced the publicists in 1930, although her first uttered words were, 'Gimme a visky with chincher aile on the side – and don't be stingy.' Who was she?

8 A famous 1957 Buddy Holly hit took its name from

John Wayne's catchphrase in *The Searchers* of the previous year. What was its title?

9 On the same subject, rock band Big Country's 1991 album *No Place Like Home* featured the track 'We're Not in Kansas Now'. To which 1939 film classic are both titles references?

10 Who is the only Oscar to win an Oscar?

11 Which movie-inspired attraction has been described as 'the biggest people trap ever built by a mouse'?

12 When the 1991 Robbie Coltrane movie *The Pope Must Die* was released in America, its potentially offensive title was softened by the addition of a single letter. What was its new title?

13 Claude Rains's 1933 movie début catapulted him to stardom, although he was only seen for a couple of seconds. Why, and what was the movie?

14 The 1945 British movie *Caesar and Cleopatra* was renowned for its extravagance. What did the producer ship to Egypt because the native variety was the wrong colour?

15 Despite appearances, Mel Gibson never said a word in *Mad Max* (1979) – how come, and why?

16 Harry Percy is a movie producer. He's also a member of the British nobility, having inherited a fortune of £200 million including London's largest private house, Syon Park. What's his title?

17 When Mel Brooks made *Silent Movie* in 1976, the only word in the picture, '*Non*', is spoken appropriately by an otherwise silent actor – who?

18 Who was awarded the newly created Freedom of Nottingham Castle and Freedom of Sherwood Forest by Nottingham City and County councils in 1992?

Still More Continuity

A further set of leading questions . . .

1 After fifty-seven years in movies, he won his first Oscar at the age of seventy-seven for his 1981 performance in *Arthur*. Who is he?

2 A veteran American actor had just pipped him to the post in 1975 by being the oldest winner (at eighty) of a performing Oscar for *The Sunshine Boys*. Who is he?

3 Of whom were *The Boys from Brazil* clones in the 1978 Gregory Peck/Laurence Olivier thriller?

4 *Brazil* was an unsuccessful 1985 movie written and directed by a former Python. Which?

5 Which animated stars won seven Oscars between 1943 and 1952?

6 The well-known catchphrase of a cartoon character provided the title for a 1972 Barbra Streisand/Ryan O'Neal movie – which?

7 Which TV soap gave Ryan O'Neal his first big break?

8 When Meg Ryan was Sally, who was Billy Crystal?

9 A soft-porn character first seen in 1974 appeared in six further sequels and even a *Carry On* film. Who is she?

10 Which military rank provided the title for the first *Carry On* film in 1958?

11 What was J. Arthur Rank's first name?

12 What is the connection between Rank films and ex-boxer 'Bombardier' Billy Wells?

13 H. G. Wells himself wrote the screenplay from his own novel for this famous 1936 futuristic classic. What is its title?

14 In the same year a leading British actress was born, a recent 'role' being a Labour MP since 1992. Who is she?

15 What is the name of the British trade union for professional actors?

16 Which Canadian comic actor was *Trading Places* with Eddie Murphy in the 1983 movie?

17 Which actor Murphy came to movies on the strength of being America's most decorated war hero?

18 In which 'War' did Michael Douglas and Kathleen Turner become involved in 1989?

19 The same couple had already appeared together in the 1985 *Jewel of the Nile*. To which movie was this a sequel?

20 In which city on the Nile did Charlton Heston meet his death in the 1966 movie of the same name?

21 Heston played the same role in *Julius Caesar* (1970) and *Anthony and Cleopatra* in 1972. Which role?

Crossword No. 4

Across

1 1978 musical starring John Travolta and Olivia Newton-John (6)

5 *The Sons of Katie* —, 1965 John Wayne/Dean Martin western (5)

10 *— of Me*, 1984 Steve Martin comedy (3)

11 Paul McCartney gave his to Broad Street, also in 1984 (7)

12 Clint Eastwood's movie production company (7)

13 Steven Spielberg's 1985 colour (6)

14 Man with whom Hoffman and Olivier were involved in 1976 (8)

16 *— for Hitler*, the bad-taste play within the 1967 Mel Brooks movie *The Producers* (10)

19 *The Gold* —, famous Chaplin movie (1925) (4)

22 *— Flynn Boyle, ex-Twin Peaks*, in 1992 part of *Wayne's World* (4)

23 The terms Shirley MacLaine and Jack Nicholson were on in 1983 (10)

25 The street Michael Caine and Sigourney Weaver were on in 1986 (4,4)

26 1991 Blake Edwards film starring Ellen Barkin (6)

29 Mr Ford Coppola (7)

31 Term often used to describe Sam Peckinpah movies (7)

32 American writer responsible for *The Black Cat* and *The Pit and the Pendulum*, both filmed (3)

33 Surname of the star of *Ooh, You are Awful* (1972) (5)

34 Rita, one of *Peter's Friends* in 1992 (6)

Down

2 Rabbit put in the frame in 1988 (5)

3 1980 Abrahams/Zucker disaster movie spoof (8)

4 Peter Fonda was this kind of rider in 1969 (4)

5 Nightmarish street? (3)

6 One of many of which Clint had a fistful in 1964 (6)

7 1989 Patrick Swayze/Kelly Lynch kung fu movie (4,5)

8 Bryan —, Australian actor, husband of Rachel Ward (5)

9 Robert Redford made an indecent one in 1992 (8)

15 Anouk —, French actress, star of the classic *A Man and a Woman* in 1966 (5)

17 Second chance to see a movie? (2-7)

18 Brando's 1972 Parisian dance? (5)

20 1991 send-up of *Top Gun* starring Charlie Sheen (3,5)

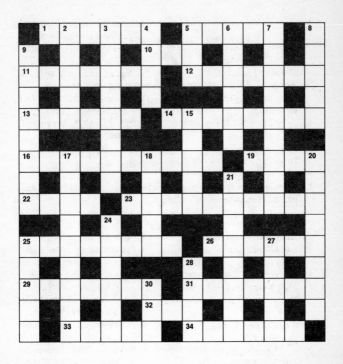

21 Surname of the actress
subject of *Mommie Dearest*
(1981) (8)
24 Don —, veteran movie actor
in *Cocoon* in 1985, etc. (6)
25 1992 title role for Jack
Nicholson (5)

27 *Being* —, Peter Sellers's last
major movie (1979) (5)
28 — *the Top*, 1987 Sylvester
Stallone movie about arm
wrestling (4)
30 One who loved 007 in the
1977 Bond movie? (3)

The Big Match

Each question consists of two groups of three; can you match them up correctly? (Some adjacent pairs are, in fact, correct, just to confuse you!)

1 Some Hollywood stars have exotic birthplaces; can you guess who hails from where?

   a Julie Christie   a Buenos Aires, Argentina
   b Olivia Hussey   b Chihuahua, Mexico
   c Anthony Quinn   c Tea plantation, Assam, India

2 Close encounters – who met whom in these unlikely combinations?

   a Abbott and Costello meet a the Invisible Man
   b Frankenstein meets   b the She-Devil
   c Tarzan and   c the Wolf Man

3 Pair up these movie title halves:

   a The China   a Contract
   b The Eiger   b Sanction
   c The Marseille c Syndrome

4 Pair up the singers with the Bond film for which each sang the theme song:

   a Duran Duran   a For Your Eyes Only
   b Sheena Easton   b The Spy Who Loved Me
   c Carly Simon   c A View to a Kill

5 Reassemble these horrors:

   a The Beast   a from the Black Lagoon
   b The Creature b from 20,000 Fathoms
   c The Thing   c with Two Heads

6 The man who . . . did what in the thirties and forties?

   a Mr Blandings   *a Goes to Washington*
   b Mr Deeds   *b Builds His Dream House*
   c Mr Smith   *c Goes to Town*

7 The entertainer . . . which star played which star in these biopics?

   a Kirk Douglas   *a* Bix Beiderbecke
   b Kurt Russell   *b* Joe E. Lewis
   c Frank Sinatra   *c* Elvis Presley

8 Who played which Bond girl?

   a Britt Ekland   *a* Tiffany Case
   b Jane Seymour   *b* Mary Goodnight
   c Jill St John   *c* Solitaire

9 Several actors have, wisely or otherwise, ventured into song. Can you match the actor with the number?

   a Clint Eastwood   *a* 'If'
   b Richard Harris   *b* 'I Talk to the Trees'
   c Telly Savalas   *c* 'MacArthur Park'

10 The following actors are known by their middle names. Can you guess the real first name of each?

   a Charles   *a* (Steven) McQueen
   b Eldred   *b* (Gregory) Peck
   c Terence   *c* (Robert) Redford

On the Town

Many movies include the name of a city in their title, but here twenty of them have been mixed up, with both the movies and the city names being given in alphabetical order. (To confuse you further, in three cases both coincide, so the titles given are correct!) How quickly can you sort them out?

An American Werewolf in Bag(h)dad

Berlin Café

Blame It on Cairo

A Chump at Casablanca

A Countess from Entebbe

55 Days at Hong Kong

Funeral in London

The Marseille Contract

Mr Smith Goes to Moscow

New York on the Hudson

Odessa Stories

A Night in Oxford

The Paris File

Peking, Texas

The Philadelphia Story

The Purple Rose of Rio

Raid on Shanghai

Road to Singapore

Tokyo Surprise

Washington Joe

Broadway Melodies

All these clues relate to film musicals; when all the answers are in place, the shaded squares will spell out the title of a 1985 musical.

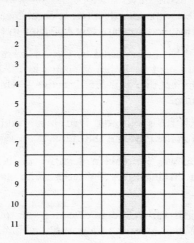

Clues

1 *My — —*, 1964 musical version of G. B. Shaw's *Pygmalion* (4,4)

2 In 1951 Gene Kelly was *An — in Paris.*

3 Dickensian Bob played by Kermit in *A Muppet Christmas Carol* (1992).

4 In 1955 'A picture straight from the heart of America' – what a state!

5 Futuristic song sung by *Annie* (1981)?

6 These 1986 beginners included David Bowie.

7 1956 fairground musical starring Gordon Macrae and Shirley Jones.

8 Surname of the actress playing Sally Bowles in *Cabaret* (1972).

9 Bernstein's 1961 story (4,4)

10 *The — — —*, Deborah Kerr in Siam in 1956 (4,3,1)

11 Seven girls married them in this 1954 western musical.

Watching the Detectives

A policeman on the lot is not always a happy one, dealing with punks, thugs and murderers . . .

1 Which real-life detective, intent on uncovering police corruption, was portrayed by Al Pacino in 1973?

2 'Popeye' has been played by Gene Hackman in 1971 and 1975, and by Robin Williams in 1980. One was based on another real-life detective – which, and in which film?

3 In which LA suburb did Detroit cop Eddie Murphy operate in the 1984 and 1987 films of the same name?

4 Madigan was a Brooklyn detective in the 1968 film and the ensuing 1970s TV series. Who played him in both?

5 Brannigan was a Chicago detective sent to London in 1975. Which American stalwart played him?

6 Coogan was an Arizona deputy sent to New York, boots, stetson and all, to escort a prisoner home. The film was *Coogan's Bluff* (1968) – who played him?

7 What is Inspector Clouseau's first name?

8 What rank was 1971's *Dirty Harry*?

9 Why were the Keystone Kops so named?

10 Sean Connery won a Best Supporting Actor Oscar for his role as Chicago cop Malone in 1987 – in which movie?

11 In 1988 Alfie and Gandhi teamed up, but *Without a Clue* – as which detecting team?

12 A dramatic and much-imitated car chase distinguished the 1968 thriller starring Steve McQueen as honest cop *Bullitt*. Down the hills of which city did the chase take place?

13 *The Choirboys* (1977) and *The Onion Field* (1979) were gritty police movies based on novels by an ex-LA cop – who is he?

14 Nick Nolte and Eddie Murphy teamed up for *48 Hours* – but which was the cop?

15 To which burning state were FBI agents Hackman and Dafoe sent in 1988?

16 *They Call Me MISTER Tibbs!* Sidney Poitier reminded us in 1970. Which was the acclaimed original movie in which black Lieutenant Virgil Tibbs appeared, in 1967?

Fresh Connection 2

Here are some more groups of three – how quickly can you spot the connections?

1 Stravinsky's *The Rite of Spring*, Beethoven's *Sixth Symphony* and Dukas's *The Sorcerer's Apprentice*.

2 *Window Cleaner* (1974), *Pop Performer* (1975) and *Driving Instructor* (1976).

3 Peter Tchaikovsky, Gustav Mahler and Franz Liszt.

4 *The Satanic Rites of* (1973), *Brides of* (1960), *Taste the Blood of* (1969).

5 The composer of the theme of *The Honorary Consul* (1983), the producer of *Time Bandits* (1981) and the co-star of *That'll be the Day* (1973).

6 The Rolling Stones' 1968 UK No. 1, the star of *Ned Kelly* (1970), and a 1986 Whoopi Goldberg movie.

7 *Star Trek III* (1984), *Three Men and a Baby* (1987) and *The Good Mother* (1988).

8 *The Enforcer* (1976), *Sudden Impact* (1983) and *The Dead Pool* (1988).

9 Simon Ward, John Alderton and, on TV, Christopher Timothy.

10 *Gone with the Wind* (1939), *Shenandoah* (1965) and *Glory* (1989).

11 Anthony, Dana and Julie.

12 The original author and subject of *Adolf Hitler – My Part in His Downfall* (1972), the star of *Dr Strangelove* (1963) and Mr Bumble in *Oliver!* (1968).

13 Michael Wilding, Eddie Fisher and Richard Burton.

14 Mork, Garp and Popeye.

15 The director of *Gregory's Girl* (1980), a TV host who made a rare appearance in *Bedknobs and Broomsticks* (1971), and the original author of *The Day of the Jackal* (1973).

16 Zsa Zsa Gabor in Hungary (1936), Lauren Bacall in Greenwich Village (1942) and Michelle Pfeiffer in Orange County (1976).

17 *A Postillion Struck by Lightning*, *Snakes and Ladders* and *An Orderly Man*.

18 Ian McKellen, Anthony Hopkins and Michael Hordern.

19 *The Green Berets* (1968), *The Deer Hunter* (1978) and *Platoon* (1986).

20 Shredded asbestos, bleached cornflakes and chopped feathers.

True or False?

Here is a collection of supposed film facts – can you spot those that are true and those that aren't?

1 Inspector Clouseau became nicknamed 'The Pink Panther' as a result of the movies' distinctive credit sequences.

2 When Woody Allen finished *September* (1987), he was so unhappy with it that he scrapped it, recast it and shot it again.

3 When Tippi Hedren was attacked by birds in a small room in Hitchcock's *The Birds* (1963), real birds were tied to her body.

4 The classic western *Destry Rides Again*, with James Stewart and Marlene Dietrich, was a sequel to *Destry* (1954), starring Audie Murphy.

5 MGM wanted Shirley Temple as Dorothy in *The Wizard of Oz* (1939), but Twentieth Century Fox wouldn't loan her.

6 Marilyn Monroe said of Tony Curtis (together in 1959 in *Some Like It Hot*) that 'Kissing him was like kissing Hitler'.

7 British movie director Alan Parker (*Fame* (1980), *Midnight Express* (1978)) began as a director of TV commercials (Bird's Eye beefburgers, etc.).

8 Peter Falk's characteristic squinty gaze is the result of losing an eye at the age of three.

9 Eddie Murphy was paid $2 million for his first movie, *48 Hours* (1982).

10 If she had lived, Marilyn Monroe would have celebrated her sixtieth birthday in 1994.

Guess Who's Coming to Dinner

... or, indeed, to *Breakfast at Tiffany's* or the *Naked Lunch*. As Shirley MacLaine said, 'The most important deals in the movie industry are finalized ... around turquoise swimming pools, where the smell of barbecue sauce is borne on gentle breezes ...' Appropriately each of the following clues leads to a movie title that includes a type of food.

1 For starters, perhaps the finest of the Marx Brothers films, from 1933.

2 For the main course, meat from a 1990 Jodie Foster/Anthony Hopkins movie of a Thomas Harris novel.

3 More meat from a 1981 movie concerning Florida high school boys who try to get into a brothel – two equally awful sequels followed!

4 And to glaze it, a seminal sixties movie starring Rita Tushingham and Dora Bryan.

5 To accompany these main courses there's a 1970 vegetable courtesy of Robert Altman, which subsequently transferred to TV ...

6 ... a nostalgic 1991 Kathy Bates/Jessica Tandy movie from a novel by Fannie Flagg ...

7 ... and Freebie's 1974 partner or Paul Newman's 1972 Judge.

8 To finish, anarchic 1971 fruit from Woody Allen as an accidental South American rebel.

Quiz of the Year: 1991

For classical stage actor and film star David Warner, 1991 was a special year: 'Now at last I can look my daughter's friends in the face. When they ask me what I do, I can say I was in *Teenage Mutant Ninja Turtles 2*!'

1 After José Ferrer in 1950 and Steve Martin in 1987, Gérard Depardieu played a French romantic hero with a facial problem. What was the movie?

2 Depardieu also starred with Andie MacDowell as a Frenchman who needs something to stay in the US. That something was the movie's title – what was it?

3 The last in a fourteen-year-long movie series featured the writer/star's son Sage as his screen son. Who is the star, and what was the series?

4 *Havana* was the seventh movie bringing together director Sidney Pollack and which actor?

5 *Postcards from the Edge* was a movie based on an autobiographical novel by actress Carrie Fisher. Her mother was played by Shirley MacLaine, but which Hollywood actress of 1950s musicals is her real mother?

6 'Eight legs, two fangs and an attitude.' The fear of which creatures gave this movie its title?

7 Val Kilmer was Jim Morrison, in which Oliver Stone biopic of a famous rock group?

8 In the movie *Scenes from a Mall* Woody Allen did something he hadn't done since 1976 – what?

9 In *American Friends*, co-written by this ex-Python, he played his great-grandfather. Who's the actor?

74

10 A great movie director died in April, having made only sixteen movies in fifty years, including fifteen years without making a single one. Who was he?

11 A romantic comedy starring the unlikely pairing of Cher and Bob Hoskins sounded as though Daryl Hannah might have been at home in it. What was the movie?

12 'The first important American movie to plop two women in a car and send them careering down open Western roads with the cops in . . . pursuit' (*Time*). Who were the girls of the title?

13 Despite being set in Olde England, there was an 'extraordinary selection of accents on offer – Californian, New York, Devon, Cockney . . .' Which blockbuster attracted this criticism?

14 'It's nothing personal' said Arnie's gigantic cyborg in what was reputed to be the most expensive movie ever made – and a sequel at that. Which movie?

15 *The Secret of the Ooze* was the subtitle of another blockbusting sequel – to which movie?

16 In the Tim Burton fantasy, the Inventor created a boy who looks human enough except for his hands. What was unusual about them?

Crossword No. 5

Across

1 Sixties stage musical filmed in 1979 (4)

4 Singer/actress, star of 13 across (4)

8 *Midnight* —, 1978 Alan Parker drug-smuggling movie (7)

10 What Morgan Freeman was doing to Jessica 'Miss Daisy' Tandy in 1989 (7)

11 *The* —, 1988 movie with Jodie Foster as a rape victim (7)

12 British actress Lesley-Anne (4)

13 1985 movie about a disfigured teenager, starring 4 across (4)

15 Kirk Douglas and Richard Harris were the heroes of this in 1965 (8)

18 Magnolia material in the 1989 movie (5)

20 As well as being a gentleman, Richard Gere was this in 1982 (7)

22 George —, *Star Wars* director (5)

25 Martin —, *Cape Fear* director (8)

28 1982 Disney computer games adventure (4)

29 Nastassja Kinski title role of 1979 (4)

30 Musician associated with a famous 1971 Topol musical (7)

32 Victoria —, actress wife of Steve Martin (7)

33 1956 circus film starring Burt Lancaster flying on it, as he did before he became an actor (7)

34 *Breakheart* —, 1975 Charles Bronson movie (4)

35 *A — to a Kill*, 1985 Bond movie (4)

Down

2 1970 Burt Lancaster disaster movie (7)

3 The Pink Panther got his in 1978 (7)

4 Movie theatre (6)

5 New version of an old movie, usually unsuccessful! (6)

6 Major biblical or historical movie, perhaps (4)

7 *Savage* —, 1972 Ken Russell movie (7)

9 The late Mr James, for example (3)

14 Rod —, US actor who won an Oscar for *In the Heat of the Night* in 1967 (7)

16 James — Jones, US actor who as well as many appearances was the voice of Darth Vader (4)

17 That of the Spider Woman won William Hurt an Oscar in 1985 (4)

18 Beau and Jeff are Lloyd's (4)
19 Miss Lane, Margot Kidder's role in *Superman* (1978) (4)
21 John —, Roseanne's husband but only *Born Yesterday* in 1972 (7)
23 British actor who won an Oscar as a Roman slave in *Spartacus* (1960) (7)
24 — *of Malice*, 1981 Paul Newman movie (7)

26 Surname of the actress who was *The French Lieutenant's Woman* in 1981 (6)
27 They had *Dirty Faces* in the classic 1938 Cagney/Bogart gangster movie (6)
30 — *City*, seminal 1972 John Huston movie with Stacy Keach and Jeff Bridges (3)
31 *Sex,* — *and Videotape* (1989) (4)

The Continuity Continues . . .

More questions hanging upon a single thread.

1 In *Victor/Victoria* (1982) which actress played, uncharacteristically, a girl playing a boy playing a girl?

2 The 1981 POW escape movie *Victory* (a.k.a. *Escape to Victory*) featured numerous real international footballers, including England's most celebrated captain – who?

3 How does POW Steve McQueen pass the time in solitary confinement in the 'cooler' during *The Great Escape* (1963)?

4 Which eminent theatrical knight made his feature film début in 1946 as Herbert Pocket in David Lean's *Great Expectations*?

5 What is the name of the Herbert Lom character in the *Pink Panther* films?

6 In which celebrated 1947 British thriller does a young Richard Attenborough play 'Pinky'?

7 Which black activist was the subject of Attenborough's 1987 movie *Cry Freedom*?

8 The Australian movie *A Cry in the Dark* (1988) stars Meryl Streep in the true-life court case of a woman who claims her child was murdered by – what?

9 *A Shot in the Dark* (1964) was one of a series of films better known by a collective name not used in this particular title. Which series?

10 The 1983 Dick Clement movie *Bullshot* was a spoof on a popular series of films of the twenties, thirties and forties featuring an ex-war hero investigator – who?

11 What kind of sportsman was Robert de Niro playing in *Raging Bull* (1980)?

12 In which district of New York was there 'a rage' in the 1991 Bill Duke thriller?

13 In which part of New York was Woody Allen involved with Diane Keaton, Meryl Streep and Mariel Hemingway in 1979?

14 What relation are Mariel and Margaux Hemingway to one another and to the novelist Ernest Hemingway?

15 Mariel Hemingway starred in *Superman IV* (1987), with Gene Hackman reprising for the third time his role as – who?

16 Which part of the USA was burning for Gene Hackman and Willem Dafoe in 1988?

17 Willem Dafoe starred in the Vietnam movie *Platoon* (1986), written and directed by a man who had fought there and won a Bronze Star – who?

18 *Full Metal Jacket* (1987) was a Stanley Kubrick Vietnam picture – what is a 'full metal jacket'?

19 Kubrick's previous film had been seven years earlier, a horror/ghost story starring Jack Nicholson. What was its title?

20 Nicholson won an Oscar in 1983 for his role as a washed-up astronaut living next door to Shirley MacLaine. In which movie?

21 MacLaine starred with Peter Sellers in *Being There* in 1979. What was Sellers's character's job that was mistaken for a profound political philosophy?

22 Complete the 1987 movie title: *The —— of Being*.

Horse Operas!

'Every story', said director Sam Peckinpah, 'is a western. You put the hare in front of the hound and let the hound chase the hare. Simple.'

1 Who appeared in several westerns as the Man With No Name?

2 In which famous 1952 western did Gary Cooper play Marshal Will Kane?

3 Which 'spaghetti western' had the Italian title *Il Buono, il Brutto, il Cattivo*?

4 Which famous 1969 western told the story of the leaders of the Hole in the Wall Gang?

5 What was the title of Mel Brooks's 1974 spoof western starring Cleavon Little and Gene Wilder?

6 Who were, collectively, Yul Brynner, Steve McQueen, Horst Buchholz, Charles Bronson, Robert Vaughn, Brad Dexter and James Coburn?

7 Yul Brynner went on to play a western gunslinger in *Westworld* (1973) – but what was unusual about him?

8 *The Long Riders* (1980) told the story of three sets of outlaw brothers. What was interesting about the movie's casting?

9 Which other 1980 western, telling of the Johnson County Wars in 1892 Wyoming, cost $36 million, was lambasted by the critics and was withdrawn?

10 Which British comic actor played an English sheriff in the 1985 western *Silverado*?

11 Which other famous British actor made an unlikely *Sheriff of Fractured Jaw* in 1958?

12 Which real-life outlaw was played by Robert Duvall in *The Great Northfield Minnesota Raid* in 1971?

13 John Ford's famous 1946 movie of the Earp/Clanton shoot-out at the OK Corral, *My Darling Clementine*, claimed to be totally authentic. How was this possible?

14 As which real-life character did Errol Flynn appear in the 1941 classic western *They Died with Their Boots On*?

15 Finally, can you identify the actors who played these western title roles?

  a The Outlaw Josey Wales (1976).
  b The Shootist (1976).
  c The Gunfighter (1950).
  d The Life and Times of Judge Roy Bean (1972).
  e Jeremiah Johnson (1972).
  f Hannie Caulder (1971).
  g Shane (1953).

Film Clips Part 3

A further helping of movie miscellany.

1 The 1961 horror movie *Homicidal* included a 'horror break' – what was its purpose?

2 Which 1986 Australian movie became the most successful foreign film to date ever released in North America?

3 One of *The Blues Brothers* (1980) had a younger brother who was teamed with a dog in *K-9* (1989). Who are they?

4 Which leading actor of the eighties and nineties was born Thomas C. Mapother IV, using his middle name as his screen surname?

5 *Somebody Up There Likes Me* was what this actor might have said when he got the part in that movie after James Dean's sudden death in 1955 – it made him a star. Who is he?

6 Steve McQueen turned down the chance to play opposite that same star in a 1969 'buddy' western. Who got the part?

7 Between 1987 and 1989 this hard-working actor made nine movies, including *Superman IV* (1987). Who is he?

8 What do Meryl Streep's roles in *Silkwood* (1983), *Out of Africa* (1985) and *A Cry in the Dark* (1988) have in common?

9 Which 1980 movie starred a campaigning actress nicknamed 'Hanoi Jane', a country singer and a former *Laugh-In* star?

10 Which actress was nominated for Best Actress for *Frances* and Best Supporting Actress for *Tootsie* in the same year (1982), only the fourth time this had happened in fifty-five years of the Oscars?

11 Which comic actor/writer/director co-wrote, and appeared as James Bond's nephew in, *Casino Royale* in 1967?

12 The much-lauded *A Passage to India* (1984) was David Lean's first movie since one in 1970 that had not been a critical success – which was it?

13 Of which major Hollywood company is Touchstone Pictures a division?

14 Which 1986 historical/sci-fi fantasy starred a James Bond and a Tarzan?

15 Which eighteenth-century French novel was filmed by a British director with an American cast in 1988?

16 Which knight played a knight in *Star Wars* (1977)?

17 Sid Vicious, Joe Orton and Dracula – all played on screen by which British actor?

18 Which country is home to movie directors Wim Wenders, Rainer Werner Fassbinder and Werner Herzog?

19 In the 1991 *The Addams Family* movie only one part of Christopher Hart's anatomy is seen. What role does he play?

20 Bernardo Bertolucci was the first Western director allowed to film in Peking. What was the title of the 1987 picture?

Hype!

Can you identify the films that carried these well-known, catchy or downright dotty publicity tags?

1 'In space no one can hear you scream' (1979).

2 'They're young ... they're in love ... and they kill people' (1967).

3 'Love means never having to say you're sorry' (1970).

4 'We are not alone ...' (1977).

5 'Just when you thought it was safe to go back into the water' (1978).

6 ... which spawned an imitation for a Dudley Moore comedy of the following year: 'Just when he thought it was safe to go back into the water.'

7 'The most exciting pair in the jungle' (1981).

8 'He is afraid. He is totally alone. He is 3 million light years from home' (1982).

9 'Eight legs, two fangs and an attitude' (1990).

10 And still on the subject of strange creatures: 'She had large dark eyes, a beautiful smile, and a great pair of fins' (1984).

11 Which 1959 cinematic gimmick gave rise to this? 'First they moved (1895)! Then they talked (1927)! Now they smell!'

12 'You don't assign him to murder cases – you just turn him loose!' (1971).

13 'You'll believe a man can fly' (1978).

14 'It's five years later and for Tony Manero the fever still burns' (1983). Which fever?

15 'I am not an animal! I am a human being! I . . . am . . . a man!' (1980).

16 'One tiny spark becomes a night of towering suspense' (1974).

17 'In a country where anybody can become President, anybody just did' (1993).

18 'Never let her out of your sight. Never let your guard down. Never fall in love' (1992).

19 The third of a series: 'They've saved the best trip to the last. But this time they may have gone too far' (1990).

20 'A photoplay of tempestuous love between a madcap English beauty and a bronzed Arab chief' (1921).

21 'Not that it matters, but most of it is true' (1969 western).

22 'It's an almighty laugh' (1977).

Biopics

Hollywood has always been keen to glamorize the life stories of the famous in biopics ('biographical pictures'). 'I have played three presidents, three saints and two geniuses,' said Charlton Heston. 'If that doesn't create an ego problem, nothing does.'

1 This musician appeared in *Sun Valley Serenade* in 1942, and was impersonated by James Stewart in 1953. Who was he?

2 A more recent popular musician, who tragically had something in common with the answer to question 1, was played by Gary Busey in 1978. Who was he, and what was the common factor?

3 When *Night and Day*, based on the life of Cole Porter, was released in 1946, Porter said, 'It must be good – none of it's true.' For one thing, an English actor played him – who?

4 As with the Porter biopic, that of Jerry Lee Lewis (1989) used the title of one of his most famous numbers as the movie's title. What was it?

5 In 1979 *The Rose* starred Bette Midler in a story based on the life of which rock singer?

6 In 1984 Tom Hulce played a classical composer murdered by his rival Salieri (F. Murray Abraham). Who was the composer?

7 Richard Chamberlain, Robert Powell and Roger Daltrey all played classical musicians in off-beat biopics made by a British director – who? (And, for an extra point, who were the musicians?)

8 In 1980 Sissy Spacek starred in a biopic based on the life of country singer Loretta Lynn. What, according to the movie's title, was her family background?

9 'They had more than love . . . they had fame.' In 1976 James Brolin and Jill Clayburgh played a real-life Hollywood couple who were married from 1939 until her death in a plane crash in 1942. Who were they?

10 The life of controversial comic Lenny Bruce was filmed in 1974 – who played the title role?

11 Vaughan Williams's *Sinfonia Antartica* grew out of the score he had written for a 1948 movie about a famous explorer, played by John Mills. Who was he?

12 An English queen and her lover were portrayed by Hollywood stars Bette Davis and Errol Flynn in 1939. Who were the real-life figures concerned?

13 Anthony Quinn won an Oscar for his portrayal of Gauguin, but which artist with a *Lust for Life*, played by Kirk Douglas, was the subject of the 1956 biopic?

14 Michelangelo was apparently a dwarf and a homosexual, so the casting in *The Agony and the Ecstasy* (1965) was a little wide of the mark – who played the role?

15 A thirteenth-century Asian warrior has been played by American John Wayne in 1955 and Egyptian Omar Sharif in 1965, of all unlikely people. Who is he?

16 Which soldier/statesman has been played by, amongst others, Charles Boyer, Marlon Brando, Herbert Lom and Ian Holm?

Colour Films

Each of the following clues should lead you to a movie the title of which includes a colour.

1 Michael Douglas as a New York cop in Japan in 1989.

2 Deep South Spielberg movie of 1985 that gave Whoopi Goldberg her first break (and an Oscar nomination).

3 Where Jean Simmons and Donald Houston were ship-wrecked in 1949, and Brooke Shields and Christopher Atkins in 1980.

4 Gérard Depardieu and Andie MacDowell as an odd couple in a 1991 Peter Weir movie.

5 Unsuccessful spoofy pirate movie of 1983 with Graham Chapman, Cheech and Chong, Peter Cook, etc., etc.

6 . . . *The Legend of Tarzan, Lord of the Apes* (1984).

7 Classic 1951 Ealing comedy with Alec Guinness and Stanley Holloway as South London crooks.

8 Mikhail Baryshnikov as a Russian émigré ballet dancer in a 1985 movie.

9 Peter Sellers on the trail of jewel thief the Phantom in 1963.

10 Extremely long but award-winning Warren Beatty/Diane Keaton movie of 1981.

11 Controversial futuristic Stanley Kubrick movie of 1971 starring Malcolm McDowell.

Private Eyes

There are as many private investigators of one sort or another as cops in the movies – here are a few of them.

1 Richard Roundtree played a black private investigator in a 1971 movie remembered for its Isaac Hayes score – what was the title role?

2 'By Gad, sir, you are a character,' says the Fat Man of Dashiell Hammett's private eye, played by Bogart in a 1941 classic. Name the PI and the movie.

3 Which slang name for a detective, with Irish overtones, provided the title for a 1972 movie with Burt Reynolds as a PI?

4 Another slang name provided the title for a 1971 British movie starring Albert Finney as a would-be Bogart – which film?

5 Reynolds starred with Clint Eastwood in *City Heat* (1984) – which was the cop, and which the private investigator?

6 *Murder, She Said* (1962) starred Margaret Rutherford as which famous sleuth?

7 Martin Balsam as PI Arbogast was sent falling backwards downstairs by a knife-wielding old lady – in which classic 1960 thriller?

8 Which singer/actor played PI Tony Rome in the movie of that name (1967) and its sequel, *Lady in Cement* (1968)?

9 Enigmatic thriller *Night Moves* (1975) featured a mixed-up PI searching for a missing girl. Who was the star?

10 Which freelance investigator was played by George Sanders on screen in the late thirties, and by Roger Moore on TV in the sixties?

Circus Boys

The cast of TV's *Monty Python's Flying Circus* have gone on to give us some memorable movies.

1 The team's first film, in 1971, took as its title one of the show's catchphrases. What was it?

2 For whom is Brian Cohen mistaken in the 1979 Python movie?

3 The music for *Monty Python and the Holy Grail* (1974) was written by a singer/songwriter who was a former member of the Bonzo Dog Doo-Dah Band. Who is he?

4 This same musician was involved on screen and TV with Eric Idle, inventing a spoof Beatles-like group – what was the group's name?

5 Eric Idle was one of the *Nuns on the Run* in 1990. Which non-Python was the other?

6 In 1986 Idle also provided a voice over (with, amongst others, Leonard Nimoy and Orson Welles) for a full-length animation based on a popular toy of the time – which?

7 In which 1988 movie did John Cleese strip in Russian?

8 In *Clockwise* (1985) Cleese is trying to get to Norwich to address a conference of – what?

9 Which 1981 Terry Gilliam film was co-written by Palin and features Cleese as an urbane Robin Hood?

10 Palin played the hero in Terry Gilliam's 1977 director-ial début, an adaptation of a Lewis Carroll poem – which?

11 Gilliam's *The Fisher King* (1991) starred an American former stand-up comedian turned actor – who?

12 Cleese appeared in the movie of the stage revue *The Secret Policeman's Ball* and its sequel (1979 and 1982). Which organization were the shows in aid of?

13 Terry Jones is as well known as a writer/director as an actor. His first non-Python movie script was for *Labyrinth* (1986), directed by an American puppeteer – who?

14 In 1987 he directed a film based on the real-life exploits of Cynthia Payne. Who was she, and what was the movie?

15 In 1989 Jones wrote a screenplay from his own novel and directed the movie. What was it called?

16 The last movie to carry Monty Python's name appeared in 1983. Which was it?

Crossword No. 6

Across

6 1979 Woody Allen movie set in New York (9)

8 Vanessa and Lynn's actor brother (5)

10 What Harrison Ford was presumed to be in 1990 (8)

11 Jack L. —, one of four American movie mogul brothers (6)

12 Miss Minnelli (4)

13 1983 movie about a nuclear accident, starring Meryl Streep and Cher (8)

15 John Wayne as — Cogburn in *True Grit* (1969) (7)

17 Michelle Pfeiffer was thus connected to the Mob in 1988 (7)

20 See 2 down

22 —*boxer*, 1989 Jean-Claude Van Damme martial arts movie (4)

25 One such lived in the Emerald City at the end of the Yellow Brick Road (6)

26 Mrs Branagh, née – what? (8)

27 Sidney —, eminent US director of *Dog Day Afternoon* (1975), *Network* (1976), etc. (5)

28 Star of TV's *Cheers*, and one of the *Three Men and a Baby* (1987) (3,6)

Down

1 What Clint Eastwood and Lee Marvin had to do with their wagon in 1969? (5)

2 and 20 across   Actress who had a medium – though Oscar-nominated – role in *Ghost* (1990) (6,8)

3 *The — Falcon*, Humphrey Bogart classic of 1941 (7)

4 *The —*, 1989 sci-fi horror movie where an alien keeps acquiring replacement human heads (8)

5 1979 Michael Winner thriller starring Sophia Loren and James Coburn (9)

7 Age range of the Mutant Ninja Turtles! (7)

9 1990 film with Van Damme as a Foreign Legion deserter (1,1,1,1)

14 1946 Hitchcock classic starring Cary Grant and Ingrid Bergman (9)

16 Stalwart of the *Carry On* team (3,5)

18 Dan —, one of the original *Ghostbusters* (1984) (7)

19 Jenny —, one of *The Railway Children* of 1970 (7)

21 Nelson —, Jeanette MacDonald's partner in thirties musicals (4)

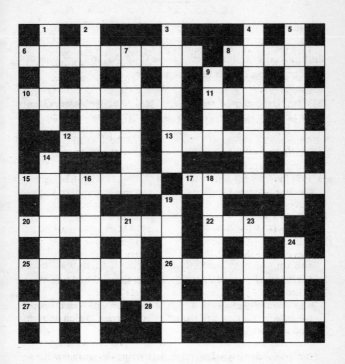

23 American gangster
   impersonated by Edward G.
   Robinson, Rod Steiger,
   Robert de Niro, etc. (6)
24 Israeli actor in *For Your
   Eyes Only* (1981), etc. (5)

Family Films

'Don't put your daughter on the stage,' warned the famous Noël Coward song, but many actors' children – and indeed grandchildren – have followed in their parents' footsteps. Here are a few examples.

1 *The Treasure of the Sierra Madre* (1948) won Oscars for father and son; the latter's daughter made it three generations when she won an Oscar for *Prizzi's Honor* (1985). What's the family?

2 Which movie actor is young actor Keifer's dad?

3 Jason was *Robin of Sherwood* on TV in the late eighties, while dad had played the role on screen in 1976. Which father and son?

4 'I want my sons to surpass me, because that's a form of immortality,' said dad, and one of them was indeed *Shining Through* in 1992. Which family?

5 Emilio and Carlos Estevez are the sons of Ramon Estevez. Carlos calls himself Charlie – by what name do we know the father?

6 Which distinguished British actor is grandfather of actresses Joely and Natasha Richardson?

7 Patrick went to *The Alamo* with his father in 1960, and David produced his father in *The Green Berets* (1968), amongst others. Who's dad?

8 Dad was *The Boston Strangler* in 1968 and mum got stabbed in a shower in 1960. Daughter appeared in two *Halloween* movies early on – who is she, and who are her parents?

9 *The Fabulous Baker Boys* (1989) were brothers on screen and off – who are they?

10 This theatrical knight's first daughter made her screen début at eleven weeks old in *In Which We Serve* (1942), but her sister waited until she was thirteen years old, in *Tiger Bay* (1959). Who are they?

11 Bridget, Peter and Henry are three generations of an acting family – which?

12 Veteran movie actor Robert Alda didn't want his son Alan to be an actor, but the latter failed as a student of what, ironically?

13 Liza Minnelli is well known as the daughter of Judy Garland, but what did her father Vincente do?

14 Another young actress who bears the surname of her father, a movie director, is Isabella Rossellini. Who was her famous movie actress mother?

15 Veteran movie actress Maureen O'Sullivan, then in her seventies, appeared in Woody Allen's *Hannah and Her Sisters* (1986), which was appropriate, because 'Hannah' is her daughter – who's the actress?

Continuity Concluded

The final instalment of the connection collection.

1 Which 1977 sci-fi blockbuster was reissued in a Special Edition in 1980?

2 Who were *Blockheads* in 1938?

3 Which 1960s pop group starred in the 'psychedelic trip of a movie', *Head*, in 1968?

4 In the same year another group made an animated film in which Pepperland was attacked by the Blue Meanies. What was its title?

5 *Blue Thunder* was a 1983 Roy Scheider/Warren Oates thriller – but what was the 'Blue Thunder' of the title?

6 Who was 'Thunderbolt's' sidekick according to the title of the 1974 Clint Eastwood movie?

7 Novelist Robert Bolt won Oscars for two screenplays of David Lean epics. Name either.

8 Lean was nominated for three Oscars for *A Passage to India* (1984), for direction, editing and – what?

9 Who was the first person to be nominated as producer, director, actor and screenwriter in a single year (1941)?

10 1941 was the year British film producer David Puttnam was born. Of which Hollywood studio did he become chairman and chief executive in the 1980s?

11 Of Hollywood, American columnist Walter Winchell said, 'They shoot too many pictures and not enough —' – what?

12 Who played the dying gunfighter in *The Shootist* (1976), released the same year that he himself died?

13 What comparative subtitle was given to the Bruce Willis movie sequel *Die Hard 2* in 1990?

14 Despite the title of the 1989 movie, we couldn't actually *see* Willis putting words in a baby's mouth. Which movie?

15 Which actress played the high-flying executive whose life was changed by a *Baby Boom* in 1987?

16 In 1986 Marlee Matlin won the Best Actress Oscar for *Children of a Lesser God*; what does the actress share with the character she played?

17 Which actress was *The Railway Children*'s mother in 1970?

18 The influential movie *Closely Observed Trains* won the Best Foreign Film Oscar in 1966 – in which country was it made?

19 The 1963 Great Train Robbery indirectly led to a Best Song Oscar nomination for 'Two Hearts' – what's the connection?

20 Joseph Conrad's novel *Heart of Darkness* inspired a 1979 Vietnam movie that nearly lost Francis Ford Coppola his health and sanity. What was the movie?

21 'Francis' appeared in a series of movies in the 1950s and a TV series, *Mister Ed*. What was he?

22 Veteran vaudeville comic Ed Wynn, Uncle Albert in *Mary Poppins*, has a son and grandson in movies. Name either.

Pardners

The 'Pardners' in the 1956 movie of that name were Dean Martin and Jerry Lewis. Here are some movie titles formed of a pair of names or titles, but like the 'On The Town' puzzle the two halves have been split and put back together in alphabetical order. Can you sort out the correct 'pardners' in each case?

Bob and Carol and Alexandra

Bonnie and the Bandit

Cohen and the Bean

Dirty Mary and Cash

The Duchess and Clyde

Freebie and Crazy Larry

Fun with Dick and the Dirtwater Fox

Harry and the Gypsy

Henry and Howard

Melvin and Jane

Nicholas and June

Robin and Lightfoot

Smokey and Marian

Tango and Tate

Thunderbolt and Ted and Alice

The Virgin and Tonto

Sevens

When the answers to this puzzle – all, appropriately, seven-letter surnames – are in place, their initial letters, reading across, will spell out the title of an influential Japanese film of 1954, and the letters in the numbered squares, taken in order, will spell out the title of the 1960 Hollywood movie it inspired.

	1	2	3	4	5	6	7	8	9	10	11	12
	2		5	7	8				15			
								14				
	1		6						16			
		4			9	10	12		18			
	3				11					19		
					13	17						

1 William, who starred in six movies based on his cult TV series.

2 George, cinema pioneer and inventor of roll film.

3 Frankie, British singer/dancer whose 1957 movie début was *These Dangerous Years*.

4 Robert, famous as 'Freddy' in the *Elm Street* shockers.

5 Mike, director of *The Graduate, Silkwood, Working Girl,* etc.

6 Peter, playwright whose *Equus* and *Amadeus* have been filmed.

7 Robert, director of *The Dirty Dozen, The Choirboys,* etc.

8 Steve, *The Cincinnati Kid* and *Bullitt*.

9 Sir Peter, Poirot on the Nile.

10 Julia, *Pretty Woman*.

11 Ursula, the first 'Bond girl' in *Dr No*.

12 Jill, former wife of Charles Bronson, who died in 1990.

The Film of the Book

W. C. Fields gave a classic performance as Micawber in an adaptation of Dickens's *David Copperfield* back in 1935, although he was apprehensive at undertaking his first dramatic role. Could he include one of his juggling routines? No, it was explained, Dickens didn't mention anything about Micawber juggling. 'He probably forgot,' retorted Fields. Many classics of literature have been translated on to the big screen, more or less intact . . .

1 Which Dickens novel has reached the screen in a classic 1948 version directed by David Lean, a musical starring Ron Moody filmed in 1968 and a 1988 Disney cartoon adaptation?

2 Which adaptation of an English novel, starring Laurence Olivier and directed by Alfred Hitchcock, won the Best Picture Oscar of 1940?

3 The previous year the Oscar went to the movie of a Pulitzer Prize-winning novel that went through fifteen screenwriters and four directors before becoming one of Hollywood's greatest films. What was it?

4 That same year an English classic was filmed with Laurence Olivier in the leading male role, taken by Timothy Dalton in the 1970 remake. What was the novel?

5 A novel by that author's sister was filmed in 1943 with Orson Welles and Joan Fontaine, again remade in 1970 with George C. Scott and Susannah York. Which book?

6 A 1992 movie of a nineteenth-century novel set in America during the English–French struggles of the

100

1750s starred an English actor as a Scottish-Irish frontiersman. What was the movie?

7 All but one of E. M. Forster's novels have been filmed. In 1992 one of them won an Oscar for Emma Thompson – which?

8 Another Forster adaptation of 1984 won a Best Supporting Actress Oscar for Peggy Ashcroft as Mrs Moore – in which movie?

9 In which 1967 screen version of a Thomas Hardy classic did Julie Christie star as Bathsheba Everdene?

10 In 1970 Julie Christie starred with Alan Bates in the movie of an L. P. Hartley novel – which?

11 A pilot can only be grounded if he's crazy, but any pilot who asks to be grounded to avoid being killed *can't* be crazy, so must keep flying! This is the premise of an acclaimed 1962 novel filmed in 1970 – title?

12 John Ford won the Best Director Oscar for this 1940 adaptation of an American classic starring the young Henry Fonda as Tom Joad. What's the movie?

13 An American novelist of the 'Jazz Age' worked hard in Hollywood yet got only one screen credit; ironically, several of his novels have since been lavishly filmed. Who was he?

14 The Indian-born author of *The Man Who Would Be King*, filmed with Sean Connery and Michael Caine in 1975, appears in the movie, played by Christopher Plummer. Who was he?

15 Which Shakespeare play gave its plot to *Forbidden Planet* in 1956, appeared in a Derek Jarman punk version in 1979 and a Peter Greenaway version with John Gielgud speaking virtually all the lines in 1991?

Young . . .

Macauley Culkin at the tender age of eleven was reputedly
offered $5 million to appear in the sequel to *Home Alone*.
Would his piggy bank cope . . .?

1 Shirley Temple is perhaps the most famous of all
  child stars. 'I stopped believing in Santa Claus at an
  early age,' she said. 'Mother took me to see him in a
  department store and . . .' What happened?

2 A former child star of the seventies made her director-
  ial début in 1991 with *Little Man Tate* about, appropriately, the problems of child stardom. Who is she?

3 Ricky Schroder made his movie début at the age of
  nine in a 1979 remake of a sentimental 1931 original
  about prizefighting. What was the title of both films?

4 The star of that 1931 movie began as a six-year-old
  'little tough guy' member of 'Our Gang' in short
  films of the 1920s, and in his late fifties became the
  editor of the *Daily Planet* in the Superman films.
  Who is he?

5 Francis Ford Coppola's 1983 movie *The Outsiders*
  brought together a group of young unknown actors
  barely out of their teens. By what name are they often
  collectively known?

6 Henry Thomas is best remembered as the eleven-
  year-old Elliott in a Steven Spielberg movie – which?

7 In *The Wizard of Oz* Dorothy is ten – but how old was
  Judy Garland?

8 In terms of their child stars, what do *Tiger Bay*
  (1959), *Paper Moon* (1973) and *On Golden Pond* (1981)
  have in common?

. . . and Old

9 'I was a fourteen-year-old boy for thirty years,' said this actor, but he received an honorary Oscar in 1983 for fifty years of versatility and he's still acting into his seventies. Who is he?

10 A matinée idol of the forties, he retired in 1970 but returned to win the Best Supporting Actor Oscar in his late seventies for *Cocoon* (1985). Who was he?

11 A *Cocoon* (1985) co-star won the Best Actress Oscar at the age of eighty for *Driving Miss Daisy*. Who is she?

12 She married her husband in 1942 and appeared with him in *Cocoon* and its sequel, as well as *Batteries Not Included* in 1987. Who is he?

13 With possibly the longest acting career in show business, she started in silents in 1912 and was still acting in her nineties. She died in 1993 at the age of ninety-seven. Who was she?

14 In 1987 that same actress made *The Whales of August* with another veteran who was then almost eighty, and had been 'queen of the box office' for ten years from 1937, winning an Oscar as *Jezebel* (1938). She died in 1989 – who was she?

15 His début was in 1930, his last film a TV movie, *Terrible Joe Moran*, in 1984, two years before he died at the age of eighty-six. Between, he'd been *The Public Enemy* (1931) and *Yankee Doodle Dandy* (1942). Who was he?

16 Ninety in 1993, he won three Special Academy Awards for charitable works and entertaining US troops; his 1977 autobiography was *The Road to Hollywood*. Who is he?

All about Eve

'Hollywood is filled with beautiful, unhappy women who have shut down,' said Michelle Pfeiffer. Be that as it may, this puzzle is all about movies with the words 'girl', 'woman' or 'lady' in the title (singular or plural).

1 Whose girl was Dorothy according to the title of the 1981 Bill Forsyth movie?

2 Whose woman was Sarah Woodruff in the same year?

3 *Funny Girl* and *Funny Lady* (1968 and 1975) were biopics of the life of Jewish entertainer Fanny Brice. Who played her in the movies?

4 Similarly, *Lady Sings the Blues* (1972) was a biopic of blues singer Billie Holiday. Which singer took the role?

5 How was Julia Roberts described in the title of the 1990 movie that earned her an Oscar nomination?

6 *Girls! Girls! Girls!* was a 1962 vehicle for which singing star?

7 Where in Peter Sellers's meal was the girl (Goldie Hawn) to be found in the 1970 movie of the long-running stage comedy?

8 What breed of dog was 'Lady' in the 1955 Disney animation?

9 An animal provides the surname in the title of the 1972 movie in which 'Lady' Sarah Miles became involved with Richard Chamberlain as Lord Byron. Which movie?

10 Another titled lady was portrayed by Sylvia Kristel

on screen in 1981 and Joely Richardson on TV in 1993 – which?

11 Glenda Jackson won an Oscar as one of two women in a 1969 movie adaptation of another work by the same novelist. What was its title?

12 How does the movie's title describe the seventeenth-century lady who was Margaret Lockwood in 1945 and Faye Dunaway in the 1983 remake?

13 Which French director wrote and directed *The Man Who Loved Women* in 1977?

14 The Ealing comedy *The Ladykillers* (1955) featured a gang of robbers including Peter Sellers and Herbert Lom. Which famous actor led the gang?

15 What happened to the lady on the train in 1938 with Margaret Lockwood and Michael Redgrave, and again in 1979 with Cybill Shepherd and Elliott Gould?

16 What sort of girl provided the title for the 1988 Harrison Ford/Sigourney Weaver/Melanie Griffith romantic comedy?

The Men

'All about Eve' was about movies with 'female' titles – now here's one about movies with 'man', 'men' or 'Mr' in the title.

1 Which man was autistic Dustin Hoffman in 1988?

2 In the 1975 John Huston movie, set in fictional Kafiristan, Sean Connery, accompanied by Michael Caine, is *The Man Who Would Be* – what?

3 What is the name of Charles Bronson's melon-grower character that provides the title for the 1974 movie?

4 In Sidney Lumet's first film, in 1957, Henry Fonda plays one of *12 Angry Men* – doing what?

5 In 1970 English aristocrat Richard Harris joined the Sioux as *A Man Called* – what?

6 Which TV 'Man', or more accurately 'men', spawned a series of movies including *The Spy with My Face* (1966), *The Karate Killers* (1967) and *How to Steal the World* (1968)?

7 Which comic duo made their big screen début as *The Intelligence Men* in 1965?

8 Which real-life couple played *Mr & Mrs Bridge* in 1990?

9 Which 'Mr' did Will Hay play famously in the 1937 Gainsborough comedy classic?

10 Who, according to the title of the 1974 Bond movie, was the man Scaramanga?

11 Which man was 121-year-old white man/Indian Dustin Hoffman in 1970?

12 What quality was associated with Malcolm McDowell's man in the 1973 Lindsay Anderson movie?

13 What kind of man was Sir Thomas More (Paul Scofield) in the celebrated 1966 movie of Robert Bolt's historical novel?

14 What aren't men seen dead in, according to the title of the 1982 Steve Martin comedy?

15 What was Alec Guinness wearing that caused so much trouble, according to the title of the 1951 Ealing comedy?

16 In the classic 1955 western, James Stewart played *The Man from* – where?

Quiz of the Year: 1992

J 13/16

1992 was the year that introduced movie audiences to a new language, including 'Excellent!', 'Way!' and 'Nottttt!'. Yes, it was the year of *Wayne's World*!

1 'Hawkeye' was played by Donald Sutherland in *M★A★S★H* (1970), but more authentically by Daniel Day-Lewis in which 1992 movie?

2 *Fire Walk with Me* was the subtitle of a 'prequel' movie to a TV series – which?

3 Which movie teamed Robert Redford, Dan Aykroyd, Sidney Poitier and River Phoenix as a group of computer hackers?

4 Harrison Ford appeared in the 'Director's Cut' of a ten-year-old sci-fi movie. Which?

5 The year saw the first animated movie ever to be nominated for a Best Picture Oscar. Which was it?

6 Tony Slattery said he took his role in the movie because it would probably be the last *Carry On* film ever made. Who was its subject?

7 CIA operative Jack Ryan was played by Alec Baldwin in *The Hunt for Red October* (1990), then Harrison Ford took over the role for this 1992 thriller. What was its title?

8 Irish actor Richard Harris, a 'passionate western buff', was delighted to be asked to play an English hired assassin in a highly acclaimed western – which?

9 In which movie did Sigourney Weaver reprise the role of Ellen Ripley, the only woman in an all-male cast?

10 Bruce Wayne became the Dark Knight again in *Batman Returns*, and villain Selina Kyle was transformed into – whom?

11 What kind of animal played the title role in *Beethoven*?

12 A Robert Altman movie about Tinseltown boasted no fewer than sixty-five star cameos – Cher, Peter Falk, Elliott Gould, Anjelica Huston, Jack Lemmon, Burt Reynolds, Rod Steiger . . . What's the movie?

13 *Far and Away* starred Tom Cruise and his real-life wife – who is she?

14 Which Australian 'sleeper' movie hit of the year was given the tag 'Dirty Dancing Down Under'?

15 Pig-tailed *Medicine Man* Sean Connery was seen in the rainforest having discovered a cure for – what?

16 Hannibal Lecter became stuffy Edwardian Mr Wilcox – in which classic novel adaptation?

A Job in the Movies

The longest credit sequence at the end of a movie was *Once upon a Time in the West* – twelve minutes – while *Who Framed Roger Rabbit* credited 305 behind-the-camera jobs. As it's time we thought about rolling *our* final credits, let's find out what they all do.

1 We're all familiar with the 'best boy' – he's assistant to the 'gaffer'. But what does the gaffer do?

2 The 'grips' are specialized labourers arranging or building sets – what is their chief known as?

3 The 'dolly grips' deal with, naturally enough, the dolly. But what is it?

4 What does the 'Foley artist' add to the film after it has been shot and cut?

5 What important job on the movie will the person with 'ASC' after his or her name have done?

6 The 'clapper loader' claps the famous board before every take. Why is the loud 'clap' important?

7 What is the 'boom' operated by the 'boom operator'?

8 Some unusual credits have appeared over the years. A dialogue consultant was credited in *Star Trek V* – for which language?

9 What is unusual about the credits for *M★A★S★H* and *Fahrenheit 451*, amongst others?

10 Cedric Gibbons is credited on more than 1,500 movies (he also designed the Oscar statuette). What was his job at MGM?

11 Finally, when Spencer Tracy was asked why his name was always above Katharine Hepburn's when they appeared together, he answered, 'This is a *movie*, not a —.' What?

The End

This puzzle, appropriately, is all about endings – last words, last scenes, 'Last' titles and so on. In each case it is the *last letter* of each answer that is important, because when you've got them all, they will spell out the famous last words from a famous film.

1 Bruce Willis apparently put his woggle away after becoming the last one in this 1991 actioner.

_ _ _ _ _ _ _ _

2 Marlon Brando and Maria Schneider enjoyed this last dance in 1972.

_ _ _ _ _

3 Robert —, 'sleepy-eyed' actor who starred with Robert de Niro in *The Last Tycoon*.

_ _ _ _ _ _ _

4 Edward G. Robinson's famous dying words at the end of *Little Caesar* (1930): 'Mother of mercy, is this the end of —?'

_ _ _ _

5 Pu Yi was the last one of answer 19 and the subject of Bernardo Bertolucci's lavish historical epic of 1987.

_ _ _ _ _ _ _

6 *The Final* — was the setting of the TV series as well as the subtitle of the fifth movie. Supply the missing word.

_ _ _ _ _ _ _ _

7 Arnie was the last one in 1993.

_ _ _ _ _ _ _ _ _ _

8 *The Last — —*, an award-winning nostalgic look back at 1950s America by Peter Bogdanovich (1971). Supply the missing words.

_ _ _ _ _ _ _   _ _ _ _

9 'Drunk with wealth and power . . . rotten with pagan pleasures . . . doomed to fiery death from the skies.' Name the city whose last days were thus hailed for the 1935 movie.

_ _ _ _ _ _ _

10 The 'end' that won Emma Thompson an Oscar in 1993.

_ _ _ _ _ _ _

11 Famous last words of a 1942 classic, spoken by Humphrey Bogart: 'Louis, I think this is the beginning of a beautiful friendship.' Name the film.

_ _ _ _ _ _ _ _ _ _

12 At the end of *Sunset Boulevard* (1950) a fading movie star, played by a fading movie star, says, 'All right, Mr De Mille, I'm ready for my close-up.' Name the actress.

_ _ _ _ _ _   _ _ _ _ _ _ _

13 The murderer sits wrapped in a blanket in the cell. The last words are in his mother's voice: 'I hope that they are watching; they will say, "Why, she wouldn't even harm a fly."' Name the 1960 film.

_ _ _ _ _ _

14 *The Final —*, last of the *Omen* trilogy (1981). Supply the missing word.

_ _ _ _ _ _ _ _

15 Glenn Close dies in one – finally! – in the last scene of *Fatal Attraction* (1987).

_ _ _ _

16 The final words of *King Kong* (1933) are: 'Oh no, it wasn't the airplanes. It was *Beauty* killed the Beast.' On which New York Building?

‒ ‒ ‒ ‒ ‒ ‒   ‒ ‒ ‒ ‒ ‒

17 'Oh Jerry, don't let's ask for the moon. We have the stars!' – the famous last words of *Now*, — (1942). Supply the missing word.

‒ ‒ ‒ ‒ ‒ ‒ ‒

18 The immortal parting words of the male lead: 'Frankly, my dear, I don't give a damn.' Name the film from 1939.

‒ ‒ ‒ ‒   ‒ ‒ ‒ ‒   ‒ ‒ ‒   ‒ ‒ ‒ ‒

19 Country of which Pu Yi was the last answer 5.

‒ ‒ ‒ ‒ ‒

20 'Oh, Aunt Em, there's no place like home': the final words of *The Wizard of Oz* – but name the character who is speaking.

‒ ‒ ‒ ‒ ‒ ‒ ‒

That's All, Folks!

Solutions

Look Who's Talking (p. 2)
1. John Wayne. 2. Alec Guinness. 3. Woody Allen. 4. Ken Russell. 5. Humphrey Bogart. 6. Harrison Ford. 7. Peter Sellers. 8. Michael Caine. 9. Barbra Streisand. 10. Julie Andrews (by Moss Hart). 11. Walter Matthau. 12. Fred Astaire. 13. Marilyn Monroe. 14. Roger Moore. 15. Vanessa Redgrave. 16. Charles Bronson. 17. Gene Hackman; *The French Connection*.

Cast of Thousands (p. 4)
1. *Who Framed Roger Rabbit?* 2. *The Towering Inferno*. 3. Michael Jackson. 4. '. . . lower the Atlantic'. 5. A sled, from *Citizen Kane*. 6. $6.75 billion! 7. The parting of the Red Sea. 8. The chariot race in *Ben-Hur* (1959). 9. *Die Hard 2*. 10. *Gone with the Wind*. 11. *Close Encounters of the Third Kind*. 12. Ian Fleming; James Bond.

Leading Ladies (p. 6)
1. Elizabeth Taylor. 2. Madonna. 3. Michelle Pfeiffer. 4. *Annie Hall*. 5. *Tootsie*. 6. Helena Bonham Carter. 7. *Octopussy*. 8. Mae West. 9. Pauline Collins. 10. Susan Sarandon. 11. Olivia de Havilland. 12. Nastassja Kinski.
Emma Thompson; *Howards End*

Continuity (p. 8)
1. Mick. 2. Charlton Heston. 3. 'Convoy'. 4. The Marx Brothers. 5. Daffy Duck. 6. Michael Palin. 7. [*The Private Life of*] *Henry VIII*. 8. *Mutiny on the Bounty*. 9. *The Godfather*. 10. Henry Fonda and Katharine Hepburn. 11. Eddie Murphy. 12. A doll. 13. Clint Eastwood. 14. Marilyn Monroe (*Goodbye, Norma Jean*). 15. Rudolph Valentino (*Valentino*). 16. Mikhail Baryshnikov. 17. George Formby. 18. *Ooh, You Are Awful*. 19. Dick Turpin. 20. *Carry On Admiral* – it's not a *Carry On* film (David Tomlinson, 1957). 21. Horatio Nelson (*Nelson* (1926); *Lady Hamilton* – a.k.a. *That Hamilton Woman* (1941); *Lady Hamilton* (1968)). 22. Whoopi Goldberg.

What's in a Name? (p. 10)
1. Their real names were the same as existing film stars – James Stewart and Michael Douglas respectively. 2. It is a pseudonym used by directors who want their real names removed from the credits. 3. It's the actor's real name. 4. Burton. 5. Edward G. Robinson (born Emmanuel Goldenberg). 6. Charlton Heston. 7. True – Madonna Louise Ciccone. 8. Woody Allen. 9. Sean Connery. 10. The Netherlands – Van Den Bogaerde. 11. Mel Brooks and

Anne Bancroft. 12. Jane Seymour. 13. Terry-Thomas (Thomas Terry Hoar-Stevens). 14. Joanne Whalley-Kilmer. 15. Mary Louise. 16. Mia Farrow. 17. Lord Bernard Delfont and Sir Lew Grade.

It Came from Outer Space . . . (p. 12)
1. *Morons [from Outer Space]*. 2. *Invasion of the Body Snatchers*. 3. Flash Gordon. 4. *2001: A Space Odyssey*. 5. Earth. 6. *Star Wars*. 7. *Close Encounters of the Third Kind*. 8. *Superman*. 9. *High Noon*. 10. *The Magnificent Seven*. 11. *Blade Runner*. 12. *Daleks – Invasion Earth 2150 AD*. 13. *E.T. The Extra-Terrestrial*. 14. A planet. 15. The death (albeit temporary) of Spock. 16. *War of the Worlds*.

The Name's the Same (p. 14)
1. Collins. 2. Griffith. 3. Anderson. 4. Baker. 5. Fraser. 6. Williams. 7. Davis. 8. Johnson. 9. Lee. 10. Douglas. 11. Scott. 12. Richardson. 13. Martin.

Tom, Dick and Harry (p. 15)
1. Tom Conti. 2. *Tom Thumb*. 3 *Tom Horn*. 4. Dick Lester. 5. *Dick Tracy*. 6. Dick Van Dyke. 7. Harry Palmer. 8. Harry Lime (Orson Welles) in *The Third Man*. 9. Harry Callahan in *Dirty Harry*.

Crossword No. 1 (p. 16)
Across: 1. *Tea*. 3. Ava. 5. Norman. 9. Ustinov. 10. Lou. 11. RKO. 12. Pleasence. 13. Drown. 14. *Roses*. 16. Usherette. 18. President. 20. *El Cid*. 23. Topol. 24. Rehearsal. 26. Ear (story of Van Gogh). 27. Elm. 28. Olivier. 29. *Dragon*. 30. Ken. 31. *Day*.
Down: 1. Thumper (*Bambi* and *Diamonds are Forever*). 2. Actress. 3. Annis. 4. *Adventure*. 5. Nolte. 6. Roundtree. 7. *Airport*. 8. *Bonnie [and Clyde]*. 15. Spielberg. 17. Hitchcock. 18. Potter. 19. *Emperor*. 21. Casting. 22. Daltrey. 24. Roman. 25. *Alien*.

A Star is Born? (p. 18)
1. Steve McQueen. 2. Christopher Lee. 3. Clint Eastwood. 4. Oliver Reed. 5. Yul Brynner. 6. Gene Wilder. 7. Richard Burton. 8. Sean Connery. 9. Michael Caine. 10. Steve Martin. 11. Sylvester Stallone. 12. Al Pacino. 13. Burt Reynolds. 14. Jack Nicholson.
(Martin Sheen and Mel Brooks are the red herrings!)

Quiz of the Year: 1988 (p. 20)
1. Tom Stoppard. 2. Betelgeuse [*Beetlejuice*]. 3. *The Last Temptation of Christ*. 4. *Who Framed Roger Rabbit*. 5. Eddie Murphy. 6. *Die Hard* (Bruce Willis, Alan Rickman). 7. Kenneth Williams. 8. Roy Kinnear. 9. *A Fish Called Wanda*. 10. *Working Girl*. 11. *Gorillas in the Mist*, playing a woman determined to save the African gorilla. 12. Danny DeVito. 13. *Rain Man*. 14. Paul Hogan; *Crocodile Dundee* (II). 15. *Big*. 16. *Bugsy Malone*.

I'd Just Like to Thank . . . (p. 22)
1979 *Kramer vs Kramer*. 1980 Portrayals of real-life characters: Jake LaMotta (*Raging Bull*), Loretta Lynn (*Coal Miner's Daughter*), wife

of Howard Hughes's would-be heir (*Melvin and Howard*). 1981 *Chariots of Fire*. 1982 *Gandhi*. 1983 She was playing a man. 1984 Mozart (*Amadeus*). 1985 None! 1986 Woody Allen (*Hannah and Her Sisters*). 1987 Kirk and Michael Douglas (the Oscar was for *Wall Street*). 1988 *Rain Man*. 1989 (Dr Ray) Dolby. 1990 Jessica Tandy (*Driving Miss Daisy*). 1991 *Dances with Wolves*. 1992 *The Silence of the Lambs* (Jonathan Demme). 1993 Clint Eastwood (*Unforgiven*).

Return of the Sequel Strikes Back Part II (p. 24)
1. *The Naked Gun*. 2. *Lethal Weapon*. 3. Batman ('Penguin' and 'Cat-woman'). 4. *Home Alone*. 5. *Alien, Aliens* and *Alien³*. 6. *Friday the Thirteenth*. 7. *The Final Frontier*. 8. Third. 9. *Psycho*. 10. *International Velvet*. 11. *2001* and *2010*. 12. The film was in 3-D. 13. *Police Academy*. 14. *The Terminator* (Arnold Schwarzenegger). 15. *First Blood*. 16. Gene Hackman (Lex Luthor).

More Continuity (p. 26)
1. Madonna. 2. Sarandon. 3. Christopher Lee. 4. Rowan Atkinson. 5. [*The*] *Fly*. 6. *The Bridge on the River Kwai*. 7. Charles I (*Cromwell*). 8. *King David*. 9. Naval Aviation Officer. 10. Jane Russell. 11. CinemaScope. 12. Snakes! (Fritz Lang.) 13. Len Deighton. 14. *Cabaret*. 15. Fosse himself. 16. Neil Diamond. 17. Woody Allen (*Annie Hall*). 18. *Raiders of the Lost Ark*. 19. Oliver Stone. 20. Arnie is married to JFK's niece, Maria Shriver. 21. Film scores – he is also one of Britain's most celebrated classical composers. 22. *Malcolm X*.

Role Players (p. 28)
1. James Bond (*Dr No*, etc.; *Live and Let Die*, etc.; *Casino Royale*). 2. Robin Hood (*Robin and Marian* (1976); *The Adventures of Robin Hood* (1938); *Robin Hood: Prince of Thieves* (1991)). 3. Hitler (*The Great Dictator* (1940); *The Bunker* (TV, 1981); *Hitler: The Last Ten Days* (1973)). 4. Sherlock Holmes (*The Hound of the Baskervilles* (1939), *The Adventures of Sherlock Holmes* (1939), etc.; *The Hound of the Baskervilles* (1959) and *Sherlock Holmes and the Masks of Death* (TV); *The Seven Per Cent Solution* (1976)). 5. Dracula (1992; 1958; 1979 (*Nosferatu the Vampyre*)). 6. Billy the Kid (*The Left-Handed Gun* (1958); *Pat Garrett and Billy the Kid* (1973); *Young Guns* (1988)). 7. Raymond Chandler's Philip Marlowe (*The Long Goodbye* (1973); *Farewell, My Lovely* (1975) and *The Big Sleep* (1978); *The Big Sleep* (1946)). 8. Hamlet. (1948; 1969; 1990) 9. Dorothy (*The Wizard of Oz* (1939); *The Wiz* (1978); *Return to Oz* (1985)). 10. Henry VIII (*The Private Life of Henry VIII* (1933); *Anne of the Thousand Days* (1969); *Carry On Henry* (1972)). 11. Christ (*King of Kings* (1961); *The Greatest Story Ever Told* (1965); *The Last Temptation of Christ* (1988)). 12. The devil (*The Witches of Eastwick* (1987); *Bedazzled* (1967); *Alias Nick Beal* (1949)).

Title Roles (p. 29)

1. *Ghostbusters.* 2. *Peter's Friends* (Peter was Stephen Fry). 3. *Hannah and Her Sisters.* 4. *The Blues Brothers.* 5. *Three Amigos!* 6. *The Untouchables.* 7. *Dirty Rotten Scoundrels.* 8. *Three Men and a Baby.* 9. *Tough Guys.* 10. *The Witches of Eastwick.*

Film Clips (p. 30)

1. 'Disaster' movies. 2. [*Murder on the*] *Orient Express.* 3. *The Graduate.* 4. *Much Ado about Nothing.* 5. [*Sleepless in*] *Seattle.* 6. Cannes. 7. *Falling Down.* 8. Phil Collins. 9. Steven's real-life son. 10. *The Bodyguard.* 11. '. . . is the hand that rules the world' (William Ross Wallace, 1896). 12. True! 13. *Groundhog Day.* 14. Bruce Willis. 15. Twenty-two. 16. A law firm. 17. Norman Wisdom. 18. *Jurassic Park.* 19. *Super Mario Bros* (the Nintendo game). 20. *Bugsy.*

Crossword No. 2 (p. 32)

Across: 8. Kathleen. 9. Turner. 10. Warren. 11. *Three Men* [*and a Baby*]. 13. Censor. 15. *Bachelor.* 16. Aped. 17. [*The*] *Parent* [*Trap*]. 19. Scarfe. 22. *Blue.* 23 Features. 25. Audrey. 27. *Big Chill.* 30. Parton. 31. Capote. 32. Dialogue.

Down: 1. *Damage.* 2. Charisse. 3. Lean. 4. Unit. 5. *Star!* 6. (Graham) Greene. 7. *Werewolf.* 12. *Head.* 13. [*Kindergarten*] *Cop.* 14. Rat. 15. Beals. 18. *American.* 19. [*The Cruel*] *Sea.* 20. *Anderson.* 21. Ely. 22. Bell. 24. *Tycoon.* 26. *Exodus.* 28. Ives. 29. Ladd. 30. *Play.*

The Numbers Game (p. 34)

1. *One Flew Over the Cuckoo's Nest.* 2. *The Magnificent Two.* 3. *Three Days of the Condor.* 4. *The Four Seasons.* 5. *Five Easy Pieces.* 6. *Seven Brides for Seven Brothers.* 7. *Nine to Five.* 8. *10 Rillington Place.* 9. *Friday the 13th.* 10. *The 39 Steps.* 11. *42nd Street.* 12. *48 Hours.*

The Alphabet Game (p. 35)

1. *D.O.A.* 2. *E.T. – The Extra-Terrestrial.* 3. *F for Fake.* 4. *GI Blues.* 5. *JFK.* 6. *K–9.* 7. *The L-Shaped Room.* 8. *S.O.B..* 9. *V.I. Warshawski.* 10. *WUSA.*

The Fresh Connection (p. 36)

1. They were all made in black and white. 2. They each played a pair of twins. 3. All based on plays by Shakespeare (*Romeo and Juliet*; *The Taming of the Shrew*; *The Tempest*). 4. Each played multiple roles in the movie – 6, 8 and 7 respectively. 5. Each spawned TV sitcoms. 6. All movie themes that went to No. 1 (*Buster* (1988); *Top Gun* (1986); *Robin Hood: Prince of Thieves* (1991)). 7. They share the same birthday (3 April – the first two were born on the same day in 1924). 8. They've all had hits with themes from Bond movies (*Goldfinger* (1964); *For Your Eyes Only* (1981); *The*

Spy Who Loved Me (1977)). 9. They were all British-born Hollywood stars. 10. They're all dogs (*Turner and Hooch* (1989); *The Wizard of Oz* (1939); *The Thin Man* (1934)). 11. Composers of movie scores. 12. The first two are characters played by Fields. 13. Characters played by Kenneth Williams in *Carry On* films. 14. Names of 'Bond' girls (Ursula Andress in *Dr No* (1962); Lois Chiles in *Moonraker* (1979); Kim Basinger in *Never Say Never Again* (1983)). 15. Each couple has been twice married. 16. Alfred Hitchcock movies (1929, 1930 and 1972). 17. Royal Film Performances (1981, 1982 and 1988). 18. They all 'returned' in movies (*The Return of . . . – 1983; 1974; 1984*). 19. *The Young . . . –* titles of movies: 1972; 1985; 1974. 20. Among the destinations in the Bob Hope/Bing Crosby *Road to . . .* movies – 1941; 1942; 1952.

Quiz of the Year: 1989 (p. 38)

1. Steven Spielberg. 2. *The Adventures of Baron Munchausen*. 3. *Batman* (Gotham City). 4. *The Dead Poets Society*. 5. He was searching for the Holy Grail (*Monty Python and the Holy Grail*). 6. Sony. 7. Four. 8. *Black Rain*. 9. Dan Aykroyd. 10. HRH Prince Charles, in a specially arranged three-hour interview. 11. *The War of the Roses*. 12. *Back to the Future Part II*. 13. *Bill and Ted's Excellent Adventure*. 14. Sean Connery. 15. *Sleeping Beauty*. 16. He did voices for cartoons, including Bugs Bunny, Daffy Duck, Tweety Pie, Woody Woodpecker, etc., etc.

The Singer and the Role (p. 40)

1. Paul Simon and Art(hur) Garfunkel. 2. Deborah Harry (singer with Blondie). 3. Kris Kristofferson. 4. Bob Dylan. 5. Roger Daltrey; *McVicar*; The Who. 6. Phil Collins; *Buster*. 7. Bob Geldof (Boomtown Rats). 8. David Bowie (début in *The Man Who Fell to Earth*). 9. Cliff Richard. 10. Glen Campbell. 11. John Denver (*Oh, God!*). 12. Tina Turner. 13. Mick Jagger (*Ned Kelly*). 14. *That'll be the Day*. 15. Elvis Presley. 16. Sting.

Know the Score (p. 42)

1. 'Pretty Woman'. 2. 'Staying Alive'. 3. Greek. 4. The film of the album. 5. *Gandhi*. 6. Maurice Jarre. 7. Michel Legrand. 8. Dire Straits. 9. They are both founder-members of the rock band Police. 10. Paul and Linda McCartney. 11. The James Bond films. 12. The Pink Panther movies. 13. John Williams. 14. 'Spaghetti westerns' (*A Fistful of Dollars*, etc.). 15. *2001: A Space Odyssey* (*Also Sprach Zarathustra*; the *Blue Danube* waltz). 16. William Walton.

Yet More Continuity (p. 44)

1. Bob Hoskins. 2. Lily Tomlin. 3. The Watergate scandal. 4. Ronald Reagan. 5. John Goodman. 6. *Give My Regards to Broad Street*. 7. George Harrison. 8. Sean Penn. 9. Lauren Bacall. 10. Robert Mitchum. 11. Jenny Seagrove. 12. Michael Douglas. 13. Meryl Streep. 14. *Cape Fear*. 15. An island off Turkey. 16. 'Take

My Breath Away'. 17. *Police Squad* (with Leslie Nielsen). 18. Neil Simon. 19. *Barbarella*. 20. Brigitte Bardot. 21. *And God Created Woman*. 22. The fire service.

Crossword No. 3 (p. 46)
Across: 4. *Hog*. 8. *Castaway*. 9. *Eraser*. 10. (Coco) Chanel (*Chanel Solitaire*). 11. [*The*] *Electric* [*Horseman*]. 13. *Crying*. 15. *Atlantic* [*City*]. 16. [*Ace in the*] *Hole*. 17. Accent. 19. Craven. 21. Zero. 22. Harrison. 24. Crabbe. 26. *Enforcer*. 29. *Change*. 31. *Casino*. 32. Film star. 33. Lot.

Down: 1. *Father* [*of the Bride*]. 2. Stan. 3. *Twilight*. 4. Hype. 5. Gere. 6. Patton. 7. *Medicine* [*Man*]. 12. *Late*. 14. *Ice*. 15. *Alien*. 18. [*The Texas*] *Chainsaw* [*Massacre*]. 19. Coca-Cola. 20. Ava. 21. *Zone*. 23. *Rookie*. 25. *Bagdad* [*Café*]. 27. *Cool*. 28. Raft. 30. *Also*.

Opposites (p. 48)
1. *Watership DOWN* and *UP Pompeii*. 2. *The LONG Good Friday* and *SHORT Circuit*. 3. *The BIG Sleep* and *LITTLE Man Tate*. 4. *BAD Timing* and *GOOD Morning, Vietnam*. 5. *YOUNG Guns* and *OLD Mother Riley*. 6. *HOT Shots!* and *The Spy Who Came in from the COLD*. 7. *The BLACK Hole* and *WHITE Mischief*. 8. *ALWAYS* and *NEVER Say Never Again*. 9. *The DAY of the Jackal* and *A NIGHT at the Opera*. 10. *NORTH by Northwest* and *SOUTH Pacific*.

It's Alive! (p. 49)
1. Herbie, a Volkswagen 'Beetle'. 2. *Digby* [*:the Biggest Dog in the World*], an Old English sheepdog. 3. *Mighty Joe Young*, a gorilla. 4. *Jonathan Livingston Seagull*. 5. *Genevieve*, a veteran car. 6. [*A Fish Called*] *Wanda*. 7. *Francis*, a talking mule. 8. *Harvey*, an invisible white rabbit. 9. *Harry* [*and the Hendersons*], a Bigfoot. 10. *E.T.*, an extra-terrestrial. 11. *Beethoven*, a St Bernard dog.

Something Wicked This Way Comes ... (p. 50)
1. *A Nightmare on Elm Street*; Freddy Kruger. 2. Boris Karloff. 3. *The Fog*. 4. *The Amityville Horror*. 5. A mummy. 6. Werewolves. 7. [*The*] *Curse* [*of*]. 8. *Poltergeist I, II* and *III*. 9. *Gremlins*. 10. *Psycho*; Norman Bates. 11. *The Omen*. 12. *Piranha*. 13. Freddy Kruger. 14. *The Hand*. 15. A hockey mask. 16. Pins ('Pinhead').

A to Z of Movies (p. 52)
1. *Amadeus*. 2. *Bullitt*. 3. *Chinatown*. 4. *Dumbo*. 5. *Emmanuelle*. 6. *Fantasia*. 7. *If* . . . 8. *Jaws*. 9. *Klute*. 10. *Lolita*. 11. *Magic*. 12. *Network*. 13. *Poltergeist*. 14. *Quadrophenia*. 15. *Robocop*. 16. *Unforgiven*. 17. *Victory*. 18. *Wilt*. 19. *Xanadu*. 20. *Yentl*. 21. *Zelig*. Missing letters: *Ghost*

More Film Clips (p. 54)
1. 2 hours, 1 minute. 2. Elizabeth I. 3. *Star Wars* and its two sequels, *The Empire Strikes Back* and *Return of the Jedi*. 4. Christo-

pher Lee. 5. The Sundance Kid, hence the Sundance Institute. 6. *Reservoir Dogs*. 7. Kermit the Frog. 8. *A Clockwork Orange*. 9. True. 10. Kramer (*Kramer vs Kramer*). 11. Steven Spielberg. 12. It was not based on an Ian Fleming book, but a post-Fleming one by John Gardner – the originals had been exhausted by then. 13. Tom Selleck, committed to *Magnum PI*. 14. Sylvester Stallone. 15. Arnold Schwarzenegger. 16. Rutger Hauer. 17. Mel Brooks. 18. C-3PO and R2D2, in *Star Wars*. 19. *American Graffiti*. 20. Michael Caine (*Zulu*); Bob Hoskins (*Zulu Dawn*).

Quiz of the Year: 1990 (p. 56)
1. *Teenage Mutant Ninja Turtles*. 2. *Pretty Woman* (Julia Roberts, Richard Gere). 3. *The Exorcist* (Linda Blair). 4. Greta Garbo. 5. *Ghost*. 6. Bruce Willis. 7. Madonna. 8. *Total Recall*. 9. No children under seventeen. 10. Coppola. 11. Dying. 12. *The Krays*. 13. The Mafia. 14. *The Bonfire of the Vanities*. 15. *Dances with Wolves*. 16. Paris.

Strange Interlude (p. 58)
1. Twelve (they were fifty-eight and forty-six respectively). 2. It was Andy Williams! 3. Telly Savalas. 4. *Christopher Columbus* (Gérard Depardieu; Ridley Scott). 5. *Tess* (Roman Polanski; Nastassja Kinski). 6. *Chaplin* (Geraldine Chaplin). 7. (Greta) Garbo (*Anna Christie*). 8. 'That'll be the Day'. 9. *The Wizard of Oz*. 10. Oscar Hammerstein II, for Best Song in 1941 and 1945. 11. Disneyland. 12. *The Pope Must Diet*. 13. He played the title role in *The Invisible Man*. 14. Sand! 15. His Australian accent was considered too strong, so he was dubbed by an anonymous voice-over actor. 16. Duke of Northumberland. 17. Marcel Marceau. 18. Kevin Costner (on the strength of *Robin Hood: Prince of Thieves*).

Still More Continuity (p. 60)
1. Sir John Gielgud. 2. George Burns. 3. Hitler. 4. Terry Gilliam. 5. Tom and Jerry. 6. *What's Up, Doc?* (Bugs Bunny). 7. *Peyton Place*. 8. Harry (*When Harry Met Sally* (1989)). 9. 'Emmanuelle'. 10. [*Carry On*] *Sergeant*. 11. Joseph. 12. Wells was the famous 'man with the gong', Rank's trademark. 13. *Things to Come*. 14. Glenda Jackson. 15. Equity (British Actors' Equity Association). 16. Dan Aykroyd. 17. Audie Murphy. 18. *The War of the Roses*. 19. *Romancing the Stone* (1984). 20. *Khartoum*. 21. Anthony.

Crossword No. 4 (p. 62)
Across: 1. *Grease*. 5. *Elder*. 10. *All*. 11. [*Give My*] *Regards* [*to Broad Street*]. 12. Malpaso. 13. [*The Color*] *Purple*. 14. *Marathon* [*Man*]. 16. *Springtime*. 19. *Rush*. 22. Lara. 23. [*Terms of*] *Endearment*. 25. *Half Moon* [*Street*]. 26. *Switch*. 29. Francis. 31. Violent. 32. (Edgar Allan) Poe. 33. (Dick) Emery. 34. Rudner.
Down: [*Who Framed*] *Roger* [*Rabbit*]. 3. *Airplane!* 4. *Easy* [*Rider*]. 5. [*Nightmare on*] *Elm* [*Street*]. 6. [*A Fistful of*] *Dollar*[*s*]. 7. *Road*

House. 8. Brown. 9. [*Indecent*] *Proposal*. 15 Aimée. 17. Re-release. 18. [*Last*] *Tango* [*in Paris*]. 20. *Hot Shots!* 21. (Joan) Crawford. 24. Ameche. 25. *Hoffa*. 27. *There*. 28. *Over*. 30. [*The*] *Spy* [*Who Loved Me*].

The Big Match (p. 64)
1. *ac, ba, cb*. 2. *aa, bc, cb*. 3. *ac, bb, ca*. 4. *ac, ba, cb*. 5. *ab, ba, cc*. 6. *ab, bc, ca*. 7. *aa, bc, cb*. 8. *ab, bc, ca*. 9. *ab, bc, ca*. 10. *ac, bb, ca*.

On the Town (p. 66)
An American Werewolf in London (1981); *Bagdad Café* (1987); *Blame it on Rio* (1984); *A Chump at Oxford* (1940); *A Countess from Hong Kong* (1966); *55 Days at Peking* (1963); *Funeral in Berlin* (1966); *The Marseille Contract* (1974); *Mr Smith Goes to Washington* (1939); *Moscow on the Hudson* (1984); *New York Stories* (1989); *A Night in Casablanca* (1946); *The Odessa File* (1974); *Paris, Texas* (1984); *The Philadelphia Story* (1940); *The Purple Rose of Cairo* (1985); *Raid on Entebbe* (1976); *Road to Singapore* (1940); *Shanghai Surprise* (1986); *Tokyo Joe* (1949).

Broadway Melodies (p. 67)
1. *Fair Lady*. 2. *American*. 3 Cratchit. 4. *Oklahoma!* 5. 'Tomorrow'. 6. *Absolute*. 7. *Carousel*. 8. (Liza) Minnelli. 9. *West Side* [*Story*]. 10. *King and I*. 11. [*Seven Brides for Seven*] *Brothers*.
Musical: *A Chorus Line*.

Watching the Detectives (p. 68)
1. *Serpico*. 2. Gene Hackman ('Popeye' Doyle); *The French Connection*; *The French Connection 2*. 3. Beverly Hills (*Beverly Hills Cop* and *Beverly Hills Cop 2*). 4. Richard Widmark. 5. John Wayne. 6. Clint Eastwood. 7. Jacques. 8. Inspector. 9. The films were produced by Mack Sennett's Keystone Studios. 10. *The Untouchables*. 11. Sherlock Holmes and Doctor Watson (Michael Caine and Ben Kingsley). 12. San Francisco. 12. Joseph Wambaugh. 14. Nick Nolte. 15. *Mississippi* [*Burning*]. 16. *In the Heat of the Night*.

Fresh Connection 2 (p. 70)
1. Music used in Disney's *Fantasia*. 2. All 1970s *Confessions of . . .* movies starring Robin Askwith (1974; 1975; 1976). 3. All composer subjects of Ken Russell films. 4. *Dracula* – all the first halves of film titles. 5. The Beatles: Paul McCartney, George Harrison, Ringo Starr. 6. 'Jumping Jack Flash', Mick Jagger of the Rolling Stones, and *Jumpin' Jack Flash*. 7. All directed by Leonard Nimoy. 8. Clint Eastwood/*Dirty Harry* movies. 9. All played James Herriot (*All Creatures Great and Small* (1974); *It Shouldn't Happen to a Vet* (1976); *All Creatures Great and Small* (TV)). 10. All set during the American Civil War. 11. The surname Andrews. 12. The Goons: Spike Milligan, Peter Sellers, Harry Secombe. 13. Husbands of Elizabeth Taylor. 14. Robin Williams roles (*Mork and Mindy* (TV); *The World According to Garp* (1982); *Popeye* (1980)). 15. Forsyth –

Bill, Bruce and Frederick. 16. Beauty Queens – Miss Hungary, Miss Greenwich Village, Miss Orange County. 17. Three volumes of autobiography by Dirk Bogarde. 18. All knights. 19. All set during the Vietnam War. 20. Used, amongst other materials, to simulate snow in movies!

True or False? (p. 72)

1. False – the Pink Panther was a diamond stolen in the first film of that name. 2. True. 3. True. 4. False – *Destry* was a remake of the other, earlier, movie (1939). 5. True. 6. False – Curtis said it of Monroe! 7. True. 8. True. 9. False – Nick Nolte got $2 million, Murphy only $200,000. 10. False – she would have been sixty-eight!

Guess Who's Coming to Dinner (p. 73)

1. *Duck Soup*. 2. *The Silence of the Lambs*. 3. *Porky's*. 4. *A Taste of Honey*. 5. *M★A★S★H*. 6. *Fried Green Tomatoes at the Whistle Stop Café*. 7. *Freebie and the Bean; The Life and Times of Judge Roy Bean*. 8. *Bananas*.

Quiz of the Year: 1991 (p. 74)

1. *Cyrano de Bergerac*. 2. *Green Card*. 3. Sylvester Stallone; *Rocky (V)*. 4. Robert Redford. 5. Debbie Reynolds. 6. Spiders; *Arachnophobia*. 7. *The Doors*. 8. Appeared as an actor for another director (Paul Mazursky). 9. Michael Palin. 10. David Lean. 11. *Mermaids* (Daryl Hannah was a mermaid in *Splash!*). 12. *Thelma and Louise*. 13. *Robin Hood: Prince of Thieves*. 14. *Terminator 2: Judgment Day*. 15. *Teenage Mutant Ninja Turtles II*. 16. They were scissors (*Edward Scissorhands*).

Crossword No. 5 (p. 76)

Across: 1. *Hair*. 4. Cher. 8. *Express*. 10. *Driving [Miss Daisy]*. 11. *Accused*. 12. Down. 13. *Mask*. 15. [*The Heroes of*] *Telemark*. 18. *Steel [Magnolias]*. 20. [*An*] *Officer [and a Gentleman]*. 22. Lucas. 25. Scorsese. 28. *Tron*. 29. *Tess*. 30. *Fiddler [on the Roof]*. 32. Tennant. 33. *Trapeze*. 34. *Pass*. 35. *View*.

Down: 2. *Airport*. 3. *Revenge [of the Pink Panther]*. 4. Cinema. 5. Remake. 6. Epic. 7. *Messiah*. 9. Sid. 14. Steiger. 16. Earl. 17. *Kiss [of the Spider Woman]*. 18. Sons. 19. Lois. 21. Goodman. 23. [Peter] Ustinov. 24. *Absence*. 26. [Meryl] Streep. 27. *Angels [with Dirty Faces]*. 30. *Fat*. 31. *Lies*.

The Continuity Continues . . . (p. 78)

1. Julie Andrews. 2. Bobby Moore. 3. Playing with a baseball. 4. Alec Guinness. 5. Chief Inspector Dreyfus. 6. *Brighton Rock*. 7. Steve Biko. 8. A dingo (wild dog). 9. The *Pink Panther* films. 10. Bulldog Drummond ('Bullshot Crummond'). 11. A boxer (Jake LaMotta). 12. [*A Rage in*] *Harlem*. 13. *Manhattan*. 14. Sisters; granddaughters. 15. Villain Lex Luthor. 16. *Mississippi [Burning]*. 17. Oliver Stone. 18. A type of bullet. 19. *The Shining*. 20. *Terms of Endearment*. 21. Gardener. 22. *Unbearable Lightness*.

Horse Operas! (p. 80)

1. Clint Eastwood (the 'spaghetti westerns', *A Fistful of Dollars*, etc.). 2. *High Noon*. 3. *The Good, the Bad and the Ugly*. 4. *Butch Cassidy and the Sundance Kid*. 5. *Blazing Saddles*. 6. *The Magnificent Seven*. 7. He was a robot in a 'theme park' of the future. 8. They were played by real-life brothers (the Keaches, Carradines and Quaids). 9. *Heaven's Gate*. 10. John Cleese. 11. Kenneth More. 12. Jesse James. 13. John Ford had met Wyatt Earp (1848–1928), who told him all about the event. 14. General Custer. 15. *a* Clint Eastwood; *b* John Wayne; *c* Gregory Peck; *d* Paul Newman; *e* Robert Redford; *f* Raquel Welch; *g* Alan Ladd.

Film Clips Part 3 (p. 82)

1. To allow faint-hearted members of the audience to leave before the final onslaught! 2. *Crocodile Dundee*. 3. John and James Belushi. 4. Tom Cruise. 5. Paul Newman. 6. Robert Redford (*Butch Cassidy and the Sundance Kid*). 7. Gene Hackman. 8. In each she plays a real-life character. 9. *Nine to Five* (Jane Fonda; Dolly Parton; Lily Tomlin). 10. Jessica Lange. 11. Woody Allen. 12. *Ryan's Daughter*. 13. Disney. 14. *Highlander*; Sean Connery; Christopher Lambert. 15. *Dangerous Liaisons*. 16. Sir Alec Guinness; Obi-Wan Kenobi. 17. Gary Oldman (*Sid and Nancy* (1986); *Prick Up Your Ears* (1987); *Bram Stoker's Dracula* (1992)). 18. Germany. 19. 'Thing' (just a hand). 20. *The Last Emperor*.

Hype! (p. 84)

1. *Alien*. 2. *Bonnie and Clyde*. 3. *Love Story*. 4. *Close Encounters of the Third Kind*. 5. *Jaws 2*. 6. *10*. 7. *Tarzan, the Ape Man*. 8. *ET–The Extra-Terrestrial*. 9. *Arachnophobia*. 10. *Splash!* 11. Smell-o-Vision (*Scent of Mystery*). 12. *Dirty Harry*. 13. *Superman*. 14. *Saturday Night Fever* – the line is advertising the sequel, *Staying Alive*. 15. *The Elephant Man*. 16. *The Towering Inferno*. 17. *Dave*. 18. *The Bodyguard*. 19. *Back to the Future III*. 20. *The Sheik* (Rudolph Valentino). 21. *Butch Cassidy and the Sundance Kid*. 22. *Oh, God!*

Biopics (p. 86)

1. Glenn Miller. 2. Buddy Holly (*The Buddy Holly Story*); they both died as a result of aircraft accidents (although only assumed in the case of Miller). 3. Cary Grant. 4. *Great Balls of Fire!* 5. Janis Joplin. 6. Mozart (*Amadeus*). 7. Ken Russell (Tchaikovsky, *The Music Lovers* (1970); *Mahler* (1974); Liszt, *Lisztomania* (1975)). 8. *Coal Miner's Daughter*. 9. *Gable and Lombard* (Clark and Carole). 10. Dustin Hoffman (*Lenny*). 11. Capt. Scott (*Scott of the Antarctic*). 12. Elizabeth I and the Earl of Essex (*The Private Lives of Elizabeth and Essex*). 13. Van Gogh. 14. Charlton Heston. 15. Genghis Khan (*The Conqueror*; *Genghis Khan*). 16. Napoleon.

Colour Films (p. 88)

1. *Black Rain*. 2. *The Color Purple*. 3. *The Blue Lagoon*. 4. *Green*

Card. 5. *Yellowbeard.* 6. *Greystoke.* 7. *The Lavender Hill Mob.* 8. *White Nights.* 9. *The Pink Panther.* 10. *Reds.* 11. *A Clockwork Orange.*

Private Eyes (p. 89)
1. *Shaft.* 2. Sam Spade; *The Maltese Falcon.* 3. *Shamus.* 4. *Gumshoe.* 5. Reynolds was the PI. 6. Agatha Christie's Miss Marple. 7. *Psycho.* 8. Frank Sinatra. 9. Gene Hackman. 10. Leslie Charteris's the Saint.

Circus Boys (p. 90)
1. *And Now for Something Completely Different.* 2. Christ (*Monty Python's Life of Brian*). 3. Neil Innes. 4. The Rutles (from the TV show *Rutland Weekend Television*). 5. Robbie Coltrane. 6. Transformers (*The Transformers – The Movie*). 7. *A Fish Called Wanda.* 8. Headmasters. 9. *Time Bandits.* 10. *Jabberwocky.* 11. Robin Williams. 12. Amnesty International. 13. Jim Henson. 14. A brothel-keeper; *Personal Services.* 15. *Erik the Viking.* 16. *Monty Python's The Meaning of Life.*

Crossword No. 6 (p. 92)
Across: 6. *Manhattan.* 8. Corin (Redgrave). 10. [*Presumed*] *Innocent.* 11. Warner. 12. Liza. 13. *Silkwood.* 15. Rooster. 17. *Married* [*to the Mob*]. 20. Goldberg. 22. *Kick.* 25. [*The*] *Wizard* [*of Oz*]. 26. (Emma) Thompson. 27. Lumet. 28. Ted Danson.
Down: 1. *Paint* [*Your Wagon*]. 2. Whoopi. 3. *Maltese.* 4. *Borrower.* 5. *Firepower.* 7. Teenage. 9. *AWOL.* 14. *Notorious.* 16. Sid James. 18. Aykroyd. 19. Agutter. 21. Eddy. 23. (Al) Capone. 24. Topol.

Family Films (p. 94)
1. Huston (Walter, John and Anjelica). 2. Donald Sutherland. 3. Jason and Sean Connery. 4. Kirk and Michael Douglas. 5. Martin Sheen. 6. Sir Michael Redgrave (they are Vanessa Redgrave's daughters by Tony Richardson). 7. John Wayne. 8. Jamie Lee Curtis (Tony Curtis; Janet Leigh (*Psycho*)). 9. Beau and Jeff Bridges. 10. Juliet and Hayley Mills, daughters of Sir John Mills. 11. Fonda. 12. Medicine – he failed as a pre-med student. 13. He was a film director. 14. Ingrid Bergman. 15. Mia Farrow.

Continuity Concluded (p. 96)
1. *Close Encounters of the Third Kind.* 2. Laurel and Hardy. 3. The Monkees. 4. *Yellow Submarine* (the Beatles). 5. A new ultra-sophisticated helicopter. 6. [*Thunderbolt and*] *Lightfoot.* 7. *Lawrence of Arabia* (1962); *Dr Zhivago* (1965). 8. Writing – adapted screenplay. 9. Orson Welles (for *Citizen Kane*). 10. Columbia Pictures. 11. Actors! 12. John Wayne. 13. *Die Harder.* 14. *Look Who's Talking.* 15. Diane Keaton. 16. Deafness. 17. Dinah Sheridan. 18. Czechoslovakia. 19. The Phil Collins song came from the film *Buster*, about train robber Buster Edwards. 20. *Apocalypse Now.* 21. A talking mule. 22. Actor Keenan Wynn and screenwriter Tracy Keenan Wynn.

Pardners (p. 98)

Bob and Carol and Ted and Alice; *Bonnie and Clyde*; *Cohen and Tate*; *Dirty Mary, Crazy Larry*; *The Duchess and the Dirtwater Fox*; *Freebie and the Bean*; *Fun with Dick and Jane*; *Harry and Tonto*; *Henry and June*; *Melvin and Howard*; *Nicholas and Alexandra*; *Robin and Marian*; *Smokey and the Bandit*; *Tango and Cash*; *Thunderbolt and Lightfoot*; *The Virgin and the Gypsy*.

Sevens (p. 99)

1. Shatner. 2. Eastman. 3. Vaughan. 4. Englund. 5. Nichols. 6. Shaffer. 7. Aldrich. 8. McQueen. 9. Ustinov. 10. Roberts. 11. Andress. 12. Ireland.

Seven Samurai; *The Magnificent Seven*.

The Film of the Book (p. 100)

1. Oliver Twist (*Oliver Twist*; *Oliver!*; *Oliver and Company*). 2. *Rebecca* (Daphne du Maurier). 3. *Gone with the Wind*. 4. *Wuthering Heights*. 5. *Jane Eyre*. 6. *The Last of the Mohicans* (Daniel Day-Lewis). 7. *Howards End*. 8. *A Passage to India*. 9. *Far from the Madding Crowd*. 10. *The Go-Between*. 11. *Catch-22*. 12. *The Grapes of Wrath*. 13. F. Scott Fitzgerald. 14. Rudyard Kipling. 15. *The Tempest*.

Young . . . (p. 102)

1. '. . . he asked for my autograph'. 2. Jodie Foster. 3. *The Champ*. 4. Jackie Cooper. 5. The 'Brat Pack' (Dillon, Macchio, Lowe, Estevez, Cruise, etc.). 6. *E.T. The Extra-Terrestrial*. 7. Seventeen (corset and tapes were used to flatten her budding figure!). 8. They all star fathers and their young daughters (John and Hayley Mills; Ryan and Tatum O'Neal; Henry and Jane Fonda).

. . . and Old (p. 103)

9. Mickey Rooney. 10. Don Ameche. 11. Jessica Tandy. 12. Hume Cronyn. 13. Lillian Gish. 14. Bette Davis. 15. James Cagney. 16. Bob Hope.

All about Eve (p. 104)

1. *Gregory's* [*Girl*]. 2. *The French Lieutenant's Woman*. 3. Barbra Streisand. 4. Diana Ross. 5. *Pretty Woman*. 6. Elvis Presley. 7. [*There's A Girl*] *in My Soup*. 8. Spaniel. 9. *Lady Caroline Lamb*. 10. *Lady Chatterley*['*s Lover*]. 11. *Women in Love* (D. H. Lawrence). 12. [*The*] *Wicked* [*Lady*]. 13. François Truffaut. 14. Alec Guinness. 15. [*The Lady*] *Vanishes*. 16. *Working Girl*.

The Men (p. 106)

1. *Rain Man*. 2. *King*. 3. *Mr Majestyk*. 4. Serving on a murder trial jury. 5. *Horse*. 6. *The Man from Uncle*. 7. Morecambe and Wise. 8. Paul Newman and Joanne Woodward. 9. [*Oh,*] *Mr Porter!* 10. *The Man with the Golden Gun*. 11. *Little Big Man*. 12. [*O*] *Lucky* [*Man!*]. 13. *A Man for All Seasons*. 14. [*Dead Men Don't Wear*] *Plaid*. 15. [*The Man in the*] *White Suit*. 16. *Laramie*.

Quiz of the Year: 1992 (p. 108)
1. *The Last of the Mohicans*. 2. *Twin Peaks*. 3. *Sneakers*. 4. *Blade Runner*. 5. *Beauty and the Beast*. 6. Christopher Columbus. 7. *Patriot Games*. 8. *Unforgiven*. 9. *Alien*[3]. 10. Catwoman (Michelle Pfeiffer). 11. A St Bernard dog. 12. *The Player*. 13. Nicole Kidman. 14. *Strictly Ballroom*. 15. Cancer. 16. *Howards End*.

A Job in the Movies (p. 110)
1. Chief electrician, responsible for operating the lights. 2. Key grip. 3. A trolley running on rails carrying a camera; the grips push it along. 4. Sound effects. 5. The cinematographer, or director of photography, the person who 'works' the camera (American Society of Cinematographers). 6. It signifies the starting point on the sound-track, which can then be synchronized with the picture of the closed board. 7. A long arm carrying a microphone suspended above the actors' heads. 8. Klingon! 9. They are spoken. 10. Art director. 11. Lifeboat!

The End (p. 111)
1. [*The Last*] *Boy Scout*. 2. [*Last*] *Tango* [*in Paris*]. 3. Mitchum. 4. Rico. 5. [*The Last*] *Emperor*. 6. Frontier (*Star Trek*). 7. [*The Last*] *Action Hero*. 8. *Picture Show*. 9. [*The Last Days of*] *Pompeii*. 10. *Howards* [*End*]. 11. *Casablanca*. 12. Gloria Swanson 13. *Psycho*. 14. *Conflict*. 15. Bath. 16. Empire State. 17. *Voyager*. 18. *Gone with the Wind*. 19. China. 20. Dorothy (Judy Garland).
'. . . tomorrow is another day.' (Scarlett O'Hara, *Gone with the Wind*.)